THE
CALC...
BUSINESS, HOME AND
SCHOOL

THE ELECTRONIC CALCULATOR – IN BUSINESS, HOME AND SCHOOL

by

Claude Birtwistle

PAPERFRONTS
ELLIOT RIGHT WAY BOOKS
KINGSWOOD, SURREY, U.K.

Made and printed in Great Britain by
C. Nicholls & Company Ltd.,
The Philips Park Press, Manchester.

CONTENTS

INTRODUCTION

The electronic calculator is now becoming part of our everyday life. Decimal money and metrication mean that a calculator can easily deal with our common calculations. The price of machines has dropped considerably, partly because of improved design and partly because as more machines are sold, mass production methods result in a reduction in the cost of each individual unit.

The heart of the electronic calculator is what is commonly called the "chip" and it is this which does all the calculations. Many calculators which look very different externally – large or small – often have the same kind of "chip", so in effect are virtually the same calculator. But most purchasers are not particularly interested in what is inside; they are more concerned with what they can use it for. Firstly will it do the job for which they want it, and then are there other ways in which it can be of use to them?

The instruction booklets with calculators vary in value; most are rather brief. Their purpose is to show you how to operate the various keys on the calculator and this they do by simple examples.

However to get the best out of a calculator you need to *understand* the mathematics which lies behind the operations. That is the purpose of this book. No-one need worry that they are going to have to study complex mathematical ideas. In fact the mathematics is quite simple and basic. This book is written with a wide range of people in mind – the pupil at school, the student at college, the businessman and the householder.

Finally, this is intended to be a practical book which should be read and worked through with an electronic calculator at your side. The early chapters should be of interest to all users but later chapters deal with more specialised interests. If you are not interested you will perhaps "skip" some of the later chapters. But it is to be hoped that you won't. Although the contents of these chapters may not be directly related to what you are doing, you may likely find something of interest there and be able to extend the fascination and enjoyment you are bound to find in using your electronic calculator.

1

CHOOSING A CALCULATOR

By the time you read this chapter you may have purchased a calculator already. If so, still read on so that you can identify the type of calculator that you have and discover a little about its operation. If you are about to buy one, notice particularly the terms used and what they mean. Sales publicity can be bewildering, and sometimes misleading, to the uninitiated customer.

Size and appearance
There are at present two sizes of electronic calculator – desk models and pocket models. The names are adequate description: desk models are about the size of a good thick book whereas pocket models fit easily into the hand, although some fit less easily into a small pocket!

The basic appearance of all models is the same. At the top is a "window" in which the numbers appear. Below this are the keys which are of two types: the number keys and the operation keys. These are often of different colours on the same machine to differentiate between the two types. There is a standard arrangement of number keys 1 to 9 with the zero and decimal point below them, although the size and position of the last two keys varies slightly on different models. The arrangement is

```
7    8    9
4    5    6
1    2    3
   0   .
```

The operation keys with signs such as +, − and so on are arranged around these number keys and their positions vary from one machine to another.

All machines have an On-Off switch which controls the power to the machine.

Mains or battery

Both desk and pocket models are obtainable in mains or battery form. Mains models are cheap to run, but if you wish to move around with your calculator you are restricted by the length of the flex. Pure battery models are more expensive to run as they use small torch or hearing aid batteries (usually called expendable batteries since you throw them away when the power is exhausted). These batteries do not last very long in a calculator and if you have this type of machine you should switch it off immediately you have finished any calculation.

Many calculators are fitted with rechargeable batteries. They are supplied complete with a small mains transformer which enables the battery to be recharged and this type of battery lasts indefinitely. In some cases the machine can be used while recharging is taking place.

Most pocket calculators are battery powered, either with expendable or rechargeable batteries. Desk models are mostly mains or fitted with rechargeable batteries.

Display

The figures which appear in the "window" at the top are usually called the display. The figures appearing in the display vary in size, shape and colour with different models. Without going into technicalities here, the main point is that *you* should be able to read clearly and easily what is in the display. Test by putting in all the figures from 1 to 9, zero and the decimal point. Note particularly if any of the numbers have a similar appearance and could be easily confused and misread.

Each figure that makes up a number in the display is called a digit, so when the specification says "eight-digit display" it means that the maximum number of figures that you can have on display is eight, i.e. the largest number that your machine will display is 99999999. Eight digit display is an average size.

Capacity and overflow

The capacity of a calculator is the size of numbers which it is capable of handling. This would seem to be fairly straight-forward: one would think that if a machine has an eight-digit display then its capacity would be eight digits. But this is not always the case. Some machines are designed to work with larger numbers than those they display. To the average user this doesn't matter very much, but if you require a high degree of accuracy, whether with large numbers such as 99999999 or with many decimal places such as 5·7269174, then the ability to calculate beyond the display can be important. Without this feature the last figure may be inaccurate.

To illustrate the point, dividing 1 by 7 produces a never-ending succession of digits. An eight-digit display machine will give the answer as 0·1428571. You may say that the bit after this is so small as to be unimportant. But it is important if you are next going to multiply your result by 7, because you should get an answer of 1 again. In fact multiplying 0·1428571 by 7 gives 0·9999997. However a machine which has overflow (i.e. the ability to deal with numbers beyond its display) would not necessarily give you 1 as your final answer. The best one can hope for is 0·9999999. The reason is that however many digits the calculator is using, the number it is going to multiply by 7 is still slightly less than $\frac{1}{7}$. We discuss this later in the book.

Certain machines have the ability to recall the overflow. As an example a machine may calculate to 16 figures but only display the first eight. However by pressing the appropriate key it will display the remaining eight, so giving the possibility of a 16-digit answer on an eight-digit display.

Floating decimal point

This feature is best explained by reference to the opposite feature, fixed decimal point. With a fixed decimal point machine the decimal point always appears in the same position in the display, e.g. with two digits to the right of it. A fixed decimal point limits the value of the machine.

For example a calculator with a fixed decimal point showing two decimal places limits the size of whole numbers to two less than the number of digits in the display, i.e. in an eight-digit display the largest possible whole number is 999999. Also an answer with a large number of decimal places would have only the first two displayed. Thus our example of dividing 1 by 7 would be shown as 0·14.

A floating decimal point machine, however, will put the decimal point in any appropriate position in the display. This means that if the calculator has an eight-digit display, the display could be an eight-digit whole number or a number with seven decimal places (decimals are displayed as 0·1234567, where the first place is occupied by a zero, so that there is no confusion). To test for floating decimal point, enter a number such as 1·2345678, then multiply by 10 repeatedly. The decimal point should move along the display each time, e.g. 1·2345678, 12·345678, 123·45678, etc.

Suppression of zeros

Zeros at the end of a whole number are significant; to omit them would change the value of the number. For example 1200 is not the same as 12. But zeros at the end of a decimal are not significant, i.e. they have no meaning and may be omitted. Thus 3·40000 is exactly the same as 3·4. Many calculators take note of this fact and drop the extra zeros at the end of a decimal.

The only time that this may cause confusion is when we are dealing with cash calculations. We normally write £4 and 20p as £4.20. In a calculator with suppressed zeros this would appear as 4.2, so we must remember to add the extra zero when writing down the answer. Note that it ought not to be confused with £4 and 2p since we write this as £4.02 and it would also appear as 4·02 in the calculator display.

Round up facility

The fixed point machine should not be confused with the type of floating point machine which has the switchable facility of displaying only a limited number of decimal points at the choice of the user. Machines with this facility are said to have a "programmable decimal point". Under normal circumstances such a machine functions like an ordinary floating point calculator. But if you are dealing in pounds and pence, say, it is not very convenient to get an answer such as £3·4317. The last two figures are of no use and can be confusing. But with a machine of the type we are describing it would be possible to put the switch to "two decimal places" and the answer would be displayed as £3.43.

There is one further feature. If an answer was £4·3786, it is nearer to 38 pence than to 37 and it is important that the machine "rounds up" the answer to £4·38. Machines with a programmable decimal point do this automatically. There is more about rounding of numbers in Chapter 3.

Memory

Suppose you wished to multiply two numbers (e.g. $5·8 \times 3·7$), then multiply another two numbers (e.g. $6·4 \times 1·8$) and finally add the two results together, you would have to use your calculator to do the first multiplication, make a note of the answer while you did the second multiplication on your machine and finally add to the last answer the number you had written down previously. To avoid the need to write down intermediate answers in this manner, some machines have a store or "memory".

By pressing the memory key the calculator will store whatever is shown in the display at that time. Other calculations can now be done on the machine and the number stored in the memory may be recalled at any required time. So in the example above we would multiply $5 \cdot 8$ by $3 \cdot 7$, store the result, do the second multiplication and to this result add the contents of the store. The memory may also be used to accumulate numbers, i.e. new numbers may be added to or subtracted from whatever is already in the store.

A memory is a useful calculator feature, especially when complicated calculations have to be done. A number of keys control the use of the memory. Usually for example M+ is "add to memory", M − is "subtract from memory", RM (or M out) is "recall number from memory" and CM is "clear memory".

Machines are available also with two or even more memories which may be used simultaneously. These are useful where the calculator is going to be used for more advanced statistical calculations.

Constant factor

This must not be confused with a store or memory. It is a key, usually marked K, which causes the machine to take a number from the display and use it to operate on any subsequent number. Thus if 6 is in the display and the constant key is pressed, 6 is now retained as a constant factor. If 2 is next put into the display and the multiplication key pressed, we obtain 12 in the display; put in 3, press the multiplication key and we obtain 18; and so on.

However this is not the same as a memory. If 6 is still the constant and we wish to multiply 7 by 8 it cannot be done.

We may put the 7 into the display but as soon as we press the multiplication sign we obtain 42 because of the 6 in the constant. In some machines the constant is retained until the machine is cleared, but in others it is possible to release the constant key and thereby clear the constant without affecting the rest of the operations in the machine. In such a case, if we had been using 6 as constant, we could multiply 7 by 8 provided we released the constant key first. But no constant key will retain a number while other calculations are performed on the calculator; only a memory store will do this.

Some machines operate the constant factor on multiplication and division only; others allow it to operate on addition and subtraction also. Some calculators have a constant factor facility without having a special key: see the instruction leaflet for method of operation.

The advantage of the constant factor function is that it enables you to perform the same operation repeatedly with a minimum of setting. Thus if you require 8 per cent of the price of an article for a whole series of articles, all you need to do is to make the appropriate setting into the constant, then for each article enter its price followed by depression of the multiplication key. The answer is given at once in each case.

Clear entry key
Most calculators have this key which is usually marked CE. It enables you to erase a wrong entry without clearing the whole of the calculation from the machine. Suppose you have been doing a long calculation and have finally to multiply what is in the display by 2·38. Unfortunately you touch the wrong key and enter 2·37. Normal clearance would clear the 2·37 but also the result of your earlier working. Pressing the clear entry key, however, would only remove the 2·37 so that you may now enter 2·38 and complete the calculation. Some calculators

have a clear entry key which acts as a full clearance key when depressed twice.

Printing calculators

These are desk calculators which print out the calculations on a paper roll. Some people feel that they need this print-out in order to be able to check the entries into the machine. This requirement is difficult to understand since all entries on an ordinary electronic calculator are displayed immediately they are made. So an entry can be seen at once. The advantage of a printing calculator is that it provides a permanent record which can be useful if a list (e.g. of cheques) needs to be presented. Otherwise the greatly increased cost of this type of calculator can hardly be justified.

Logic

The method by which a calculator works out problems is known as the logic of the machine. This need concern us in one respect only. There are two main types of calculator logic and they affect the way in which you enter calculations into the machine; there is a slight difference between the two. The matter is dealt with at length in the next chapter. Briefly a machine with *algebraic logic* (sometimes called *full flow arithmetic*) performs calculations as they are written, e.g. $4 + 6 - 2 \times 3 = 24$, whereas a machine with *arithmetic logic* does multiplication and division in this manner but operates addition and subtraction by entering the number first and then giving the operation or command, e.g. $24 + 18 - = 6$.

Finally, if your calculator has an instruction booklet, study it carefully, since machines differ slightly in operation. Also some calculators have additional keys and features to the basic ones described above. The real way to understandy our calculator is to use it to do simple examples. The next chapter should help you in this early work. Numbered examples given from now on in the text for you to try have their answers given at the end of the book.

2

GETTING TO KNOW YOUR CALCULATOR – BASIC OPERATIONS

The purpose of this chapter is to ensure that you have a clear understanding of how your calculator works and can operate it with ease. It will deal with the four basic operations of addition, subtraction, multiplication and division, since most of what follows depends on these.

First of all, when practising or trying out new techniques on your calculator, try them initially with simple whole numbers which you can calculate in your head so that you know what answers to expect and can easily discover what has happened under any operation. For example, it is so much easier to divide 8 by 2 than to divide 8·5637 by 2·1643, and you know from your answer whether you have handled your machine correctly.

Clearing the calculator

All calculators have a "clear" key which clears the machine of previous working. Develop the habit of touching the clear key before starting any calculation. The reason for this is obvious. Notice that machines with a memory have a separate clear key for the memory and what has been said applies equally to this key.

Two types of calculator operation

What sort of logic does your calculator use? By "logic" we mean the method of operation within the machine. We are not really interested in the internal mechanics, but we need to know the type of logic because it affects the order in which we press the keys. Broadly speaking there are two types of logic and consequently two main types of machine.

Look at the main operating keys on your calculator. Some machines have five keys marked $+$ $-$ $\times$ $\div$ and $=$ while others have only four keys which are $\times$ $\div$, then $+$ and $=$ on one key, with $-$ and $=$ on another. (In future we shall denote these latter two keys as $+=$ and $-=$). The first type of key notation usually indicates a machine which has "full flow arithmetic" while the second one has not. Often the first is said to have algebraic logic and the second type is said to have arithmetic logic. Usually (but not always) pocket calculators work by algebraic logic and desk calculators by arithmetic logic. However neither the markings of the keys nor the size of the machine definitely fix the type and the only sure way is to test by operating the calculator.

Everyone understands the simple mathematical equation $3 + 4 = 7$ and on both types of calculator, pressing the keys in the order 3, $+$, 4 and $=$ should give the answer 7 (if you have a machine with $+=$ and $-=$ be sure to press the $+=$ when you come to the equal sign). But the difference between the two types of machine becomes obvious with subtraction.

Suppose we are working out $9 - 6 = 3$. Press the keys in the order 9, $-$ (or $-=$), 6, $=$ (or $+=$). If the answer comes to 3 you are operating a machine with algebraic logic. Other readers may be rather surprised to find that they have got an answer of -3. There is no need to worry, as this simply indicates that the machine is of the other type and you have operated the keys in the wrong manner for that particular machine. The great advantage of the machine with algebraic logic is that it enables you to operate the keys in exactly the same order as if you were writing down the problem on paper using numbers and symbols.

Doing the same subtraction problem on a calculator which operates by arithmetic logic requires a slight adjustment of one's way of thinking. Regard the calculator as a machine into which you are feeding numbers and it is going to produce something at the end (your answer). Then if you are going to take 6 from 9, proceed as follows: Press the 9 key. You are adding this number into the machine, so press the key with the + on it. Now press the 6 key. You are going to take this from what is already in the machine so press the key with − on it. You should then have the answer 3.

The operation of the two machines may be set out alongside each other where the column "Key" indicates which key to press and the column headed "Display" shows what number is in the display when they key has been pressed.

ALGEBRAIC		ARITHMETIC	
Key	*Display*	*Key*	*Display*
9	9	9	9
−	9	+=	9
6	6	6	6
=	3	−=	3

With multiplication and division (as with addition) there is little difference in operation of the two types. For example:

ALGEBRAIC		ARITHMETIC	
Key	*Display*	*Key*	*Display*
5	5	5	5
×	5	×	5
7	7	7	7
=	35	+=	35

If you are not already familiar with methods of working simple examples such as these on your calculator, you should practise some involving the four basic rules so that you are fully competent before reading further. A few examples are given below but you can make up many more of the same type for yourself.

$$7 + 5 \qquad 7 - 5 \qquad 5 - 7 \qquad 12 \times 3 \qquad 3 \times 12$$
$$12 \div 3 \qquad 3 \div 12 \qquad 8 \times 5 \qquad 8 \div 5 \qquad 5 \div 8$$

Next, examples where a series of operations is done in succession. For instance, you may wish to add two numbers and multiply the result by a third number. An example might be $5 + 7$ and the result muliplied by 3. The answer to the addition will be 12 and the final result will be 36. If your machine has algebraic logic you operate the keys in the exact order of the problem. If you pressed the keys in that order on a machine with arithmetic logic the answer displayed would be 21. Can you spot what has happened? The correct method for each machine is set out below:

ALGEBRAIC		ARITHMETIC	
Key	*Display*	*Key*	*Display*
5	5	5	5
+	5	+=	5
7	7	7	7
×	12	+=*	12
3	3	×	12
=	36	3	3
		+=	36

Notice that in the case of the machine with arithmetic logic it is necessary to press the += key to obtain the intermediate answer 12 before multiplying by the 3. Failure to do this means that in the last part of the operations you are simply multiplying 7 by 3. The other machine did not require this step but continued the calculation, and is for this reason that these machines are sometimes called calculators with "full flow arithmetic."

In a later chapter (Chapter 15) we are doing a calculation which requires 7 to be divided by $2 \cdot 5$, then $2 \cdot 5$ to be added and the result divided by 2. Now you know which type of logic operates in your machine, you may care to try the example before reading further. If your machine has arithmetic logic you will have to take care to obtain intermediate answers, particularly prior to the final division. Once more, in order to illustrate the difference in operation of the two types of machine, the key operation and display is given below.

ALGEBRAIC		ARITHMETIC	
Key	*Display*	*Key*	*Display*
7	7	7	7
÷	7	÷	7
2·5	2·5	2·5	2·5
+	2·8	+=	2·8
2·5	2·5	2·5	2·5
÷	5·3	+=	5·3
2	2	÷	5·3
=	2·65	2	2
		+=	2·65

You will notice that the machine using full flow arithmetic takes one step less.

Division notation

There are many ways of writing down a division problem in mathematics and one way has been used already in this chapter, i.e. the notation ÷. Thus 3 divided by 4 may be written 3 ÷ 4. Another way is to express it as a fraction, thus $\frac{3}{4}$. Some people who are not particularly good at mathematics have difficulty in thinking of a fraction in this way. If you have this difficulty, consider a simple fraction such as one-quarter. Writing it as $\frac{1}{4}$ and regarding this as 1 divided by 4, notice that this does represent what we normally understand by a quarter, i.e. a fourth part of a whole one. Similarly $\frac{3}{5}$ is a fifth part of three whole ones, or 3 divided by 5.

This idea is important because calculators do not work in fractions, so any fraction we meet has to be turned into a decimal; the calculator will do the conversion easily. Remembering what is said above about fractions and supposing we had to change $\frac{3}{8}$ to a decimal, all we need to do is to divide 3 by 8 using the calculator. The answer comes on the display as $0 \cdot 375$. Once more you should practise if you wish to familiarize yourself with the technique.

Try examples such as $\frac{2}{5}$, $\frac{5}{8}$, $\frac{7}{16}$, $\frac{3}{4}$, $\frac{1}{3}$, $\frac{5}{6}$, $\frac{7}{12}$, $\frac{8}{5}$, $\frac{9}{4}$. Notice that in some cases we have an answer which does not terminate because such fractions cannot be expressed exactly in decimal form (a so-called recurring decimal). Such an example is $\frac{1}{3}$. Notice also that the two last examples given are improper fractions (i.e. the number above the line is greater than the number below) and in these cases part of your answer is a whole number, e.g. $\frac{8}{5} = 1 \cdot 6$.

To evaluate a mixed number such as $2\frac{5}{8}$ on the calculator, start with the fraction and work this out, then add the whole number. An example at the start of the next chapter does this when working out the value of $2\frac{5}{8} \times 984$.

Order of operations
When dealing with an example involving a succession of operations be certain that you know what you are being asked to do. If the calculations result from your own work, you are probably fairly clear about this, but if the problem has been written down by someone else it may be ambiguous.

For example, $3 + 4 - 5$ can cause no doubts, but $3 + 4 \times 5$ is a different matter. Does this mean 3 added to 4 and the result multiplied by 5? In this case the answer is 35. Or does it mean 3 added to the result of 4 multiplied by 5? Here the answer is 23.

We noted above that when dealing with mixed numbers such as $2\frac{5}{8}$ we do not always set the numbers into the calculator in the order in which they are written. The example just given is such a case. It is normal practice to regard the problem $3 + 4 \times 5$ as meaning the second of the two stated alternatives because we usually do multiplication and division before addition and subtraction. So we would enter 4 into the calculator, multiplying by 5 and then add 3, giving an answer of 23.

But our intentions can be made clear by the use of brackets because another rule is that we work out the contents of brackets first. For example, we could have written $3 + (4 \times 5)$. This indicates that the 4 is multiplied by the 5 but the 3 is not. If we had required the calculation which gives an answer of 35, we would have written $(3 + 4) \times 5$.

An example of a more complicated type of calculation is now given complete with working on the two different types of machine. Once again, the machine with algebraic logic takes one step less.

The problem is to find the value of
$$(3 \times 4 - 2 + 8) \div 6$$
Notice that the use of brackets and order of writing makes the problem unambiguous.

ALGEBRAIC		ARITHMETIC	
Key	*Display*	*Key*	*Display*
3	3	3	3
×	3	×	3
4	4	4	4
−	12	+=	12
2	2	2	2
+	10	−=	10
8	8	8	8
÷	18	+=	18
6	6	÷	18
=	3	6	6
		+=	3

Some examples to try

2a $(5 + 3 - 2) \times 3$

2b $(8 \times 7 - 6) \div 5$

Instead of using brackets in the last example we could have written it as a fraction, thus

$$\frac{8 \times 7 - 6}{5}$$

2c Try

$$\frac{(6 + 3) \times 8}{12}$$

Fractions will be covered more fully in the next chapter and also special ways of dealing with various problems. We are mainly concerned in this chapter with understanding the basic operation of the machine. So far we have dealt with the four basic function keys of addition, subtraction, multiplication and division. These are on all calculators. Usually, however, there are certain additional operation keys even on the simplest calculators. One of these is the constant factor key, usually marked K. Many machines can also make use of a constant facility but do so without having a separate key.

Calculations with a constant

The value of being able to enter a constant into your machine is that you may use it repeatedly, thereby shortening many operations. To find a Value Added Tax of 8 per cent on any article you multiply the cost by $0 \cdot 08$. If you are finding the tax of a large number of articles you can enter $0 \cdot 08$ as your constant and then simply multiply this repeatedly by the cost of the various items.

The constant works in different ways on different calculators so it is important to find out exactly how it is used on your calculator, if it has this facilitiy. Refer to the instruction leaflet and to the explanation below.

1. Calculators with a constant key (usually denoted by K).
   (a) Direct entry of the constant. A number is entered in the machine (in some cases you have to press the = key next) and then the K key is pressed. The constant is now retained; suppose it was 5. By pressing a key (say 4) followed by the multiplication key, you obtain the result of multiplying 4 by 5, i.e. 20. In some machines the order may be reversed, i.e. press the multiplication key, then 4. Five times other numbers may now be obtained in exactly the same way. Note that the factor 5 is held until the machine is cleared. This means that you cannot multiply other numbers (e.g. 8 times 9) as long as the 5 is held in the factor.
   (b) Calculators which can release the constant. The constant key on these machines usually locks down; in other words when you first press it, it stays depressed until you press it again to release it. The machine works much the same was as that described above but with this type of machine it is possible to clear the constant factor from the calculator without having to clear the machine. This can be useful if you have been using the constant and then wish to do further calculation using that result.
2. Calculators which do not have a constant key.
   These machines retain the first factor of a multiplication calculation so that it can be used again if required. For example, enter 5 and press the multiplication key, then 3 and =. The answer in the display is 15. Now to multiply 7 by 5, without clearing the machine, press 7 and =, and the answer 35 should be in the display. Next press 9 and = and 45 is given as the result of multiplying 9 by 5. The constant is lost as soon as the clearance key is pressed.

So far we have dealt with multiplication by a constant but it applies equally well to division. There may be slight alterations

in methods of operation, e.g. machines in (2) above must have
the required constant divider entered as the *second* figure and
not first as with multiplication.

All machines which can use a constant operate it on multiplication and division, but some do not allow you to operate
it with addition and subtraction also. However you are less
likely to need the constant in addition and subtraction than in
multiplication and division.

As stated before it is important that you experiment with
your own calculator so that you are fully conversant with its
method of operation and this is particularly true in the case of
the constant where the method of its operation can vary so much
with different machines. The examples which follow will
help you.

Suppose a series of numbers has to be multiplied by 52.
(They may be certain figures relating to a week and you wish
to find the corresponding figures for a year.) Enter 52 as your
constant. Now using the method appropriate to your machine,
multiply in turn by 27, 46 and 81. The answers are 1404, 2392
and 4212.

Find $\frac{3}{4}$ of 48, 72, 88 and 55. Since $\frac{3}{4}$ is 0·75 (if you are
uncertain, use your calculator to divide 3 by 4), enter 0·75
as your constant. Then multiply this in turn by 48, 72, 88 and
55. The answers are 36, 54, 66, 41·25. Next find $\frac{1}{5}$ of the same
numbers. There are two ways of working:

(a) one-fifth is 0·2, so proceed as above with 0·2 instead of
0·75;

(b) finding one-fifth means that you are dividing by 5, so in
this case you may use 5 as your constant divisor, dividing 48,
72, 88 and 55 by it in turn. The answers are 9·6, 14·4, 17·6
and 11.

A word of warning is necessary. The constant key is not a
memory in the true sense of the word and it cannot be used to
store a number while other calculations are being performed

on the calculator. Depending on the type of calculator, either the constant is lost as soon as other operations are being done, or it is impossible to do other operations until the constant has been cleared from the machine.

The following is an interesting use of the constant facility. Enter 3 as constant and multiply 3 by that constant. Next multiply your result by 3 and then that result by 3 and so on by making use of the constant. You should obtain the following series of numbers: 3, 9, 27, 81, 243, 729, 2187, 6561, 19683, 59049, etc. What are these? Since we have multiplied by 3 each time, we have obtained the powers of 3, i.e.

$$3^1 = 3$$
$$3^2 = 9$$
$$3^3 = 27$$
$$3^4 = 81$$
$$3^5 = 243$$
$$\cdots\cdots\cdots$$
$$3^{10} = 59049$$
$$\cdots\cdots\cdots$$

Try finding the powers of various numbers for yourself.

Your may also care to work out this problem about yourself. You have 2 parents. Each of them had two parents, so you have 2×2 i.e. 2^2 or 4 grandparents. Now each of your grandparents had two parents, so you have $2 \times 2 \times 2$, i.e. 2^3 or 8 great grand-parents. Set the problem on your calculator and start working out statistics about your ancestors!

Another use of the constant in the calculator is given below.

Reciprocals

Some machines have a reciprocal key. This can be useful in complex calculations. A reciprocal is what is obtained when unity (i.e. the number one) is divided by a particular number. Thus the reciprocal of 2 is $\frac{1}{2}$ or 0·5. The reciprocal of 8 is $\frac{1}{8}$ or

0·125. To obtain the latter, simply enter 8, then press the reciprocal key. Some algebraic logic machines give reciprocals by pressing ÷ followed by =; with these you would enter 8, press ÷ and = and obtain 0·125.

One practical use of reciprocals is in foreign currency exchange. This is usually given as how much of one currency you would get in exchange for one unit of another currency. For example you may be given the rate as 2·4 U.S. dollars for £1. But you may wish to know how much you would get for one dollar. This will be £$\frac{1}{2·4}$ or the reciprocal of 2·4. This is £0·4166666, or 42 pence, to the nearest penny. Similarly, given that 10·94 French francs are equivalalent to £1, finding the reciprocal gives us 9·14076 pence as equivalent to 1 franc (or 9p to the nearest penny).

The reciprocal of any fraction inverts the fraction, i.e. turns it upside down. Thus the reciprocal of $\frac{3}{5}$ will be $\frac{5}{3}$. Working this in decimals, the reciprocal of 0·6 will be 1·6666666 . . . and you should try this on your machine.

The facility to find reciprocals by itself does not have a great value unless you need to find reciprocals as part of your work. But it can be used in complex calculations sometimes. Take for example $\frac{2}{5 + 7}$. To work out this problem you must start with the denominator, i.e. 5 + 7. But now you wish to divide this *into* 2. Having added 5 and 7 and got 12, you cannot press the division key and then 2, since this divides 12 by 2 and not 2 by 12. The easy method is to obtain 12, press the reciprocal key (which gives 0·0833333), then multiply by 2. In other words you have used your reciprocal key to work out $\frac{1}{5 + 7}$, then multiplied by 2. Alternatively, of course, you *could* have worked out 12 divided by 2 and found the reciprocal of the answer. By this method you are evaluating $\dfrac{5 + 7}{2}$ and then using the reciprocal key to invert the fraction. You should try one or two simple examples of this type which you make up yourself, but more complex examples will be found in the next chapter.

Meanwhile those who have a calculator which does not have a reciprocal key nor other methods of finding them, should note that reciprocals may be obtained easily by use of the constant facility. Suppose on a machine fitted with a constant K key we require the reciprocal of 4. Enter 4 as your constant. Press the division key; the display should read 1. You have divided 4 by itself. Now press the division key again and you obtain the reciprocal 0·25, since you have divided 1 by 4. So to obtain reciprocals: enter the number as a constant and press the division key twice. Hence we may work out the example $\dfrac{2}{5 + 7}$ by adding 5 and 7, pressing the K key, then the division key twice, and finally the multiplication key, 2 and $=$ (or $+=$). On machines without a K key, but which provide a constant division facility in another way, similar methods of obtaining reciprocals will be found possible.

Percentages

Some calculators have a percentage key. This allows you automatically to find a given percentage of any quantity or to add (or subtract) a given percentage to a certain quantity. However, if one understands what percentages are and how they work, it is possible to work them out just as easily with an ordinary four-function calculator which does not have a percentage key. This will be explained fully in the next chapter.

At this stage it is important that you should be able to operate your calculator with ease. If you cannot, then try more examples of the types given above. It is easy to make up your own examples and work them out on the machine. The rest of the book is going to deal particularly with the use of your calculator for certain types of calculation. This means that we shall be more concerned with understanding the mathematics and the calculator will be used to help us with the "difficult bits"! So play about with simple calculations until you are completely familiar with your machine.

3

FRACTIONS, DECIMALS AND PERCENTAGES

The earlier chapters have considered the basic operation of a calculator and now we turn to its use in a variety of situations. Many of these are commercial, scientific or mathematical. But in all these applications it is impossible to proceed far without meeting the idea of some given part of a whole quantity. In this chapter we shall be concerned with the different ways of expressing and finding these parts.

The last chapter dealt briefly with the idea of a fraction. The simplest fractions are those where the numerator (i.e. the upper part) is 1, e.g. $\frac{1}{2}$, $\frac{1}{4}$, $\frac{1}{20}$, $\frac{1}{85}$. This simply means that we have divided a whole quantity – one (or unity) – by the number in the denominator (or lower part) of the fraction. Thus the first fraction above represents a whole quantity divided equally into two parts: each part being a half. The second fraction is when a whole is divided into four equal parts and so on.

Turning to fractions such as $\frac{3}{4}$, we may regard this in two ways. It may be considered as the division of the whole into quarters and then taking three of those quarters, or we may start by thinking of three whole quantities (e.g. apples) and then dividing the entire quantity by four.

These ideas are basic to the whole matter of fractions, decimals and percentages.

Fractions and decimals

All calculators operate in decimals; without doubt you will accept this statement. Strictly speaking, though, we ought to say that "all calculators operate in decimal fractions". Decimal fractions is the true mathematical term and the only way in which they differ from what we usually understand by the word "fraction" is in the way we write them. There is also a restriction: decimal fractions are always in powers of ten, i.e. tenths, hundredths, thousandths and so on. In otherwords the denominators are always multiples of ten. But we don't write down the denominators. 0·1 represents one-tenth, 0·12 represents twelve hundredths, 0·123 is 123 thousandths, and so on.

Conversion into decimals was mentioned in the last chapter and is easily achieved with the calculator; e.g. to find $\frac{5}{16}$ as a decimal, enter 5 and divide by 16. The example just given works out exactly to 0·3125, but there are fractions which do not give an exact answer as a decimal, e.g. thirds. Such fractions give "recurring" decimals; e.g. two-thirds is 0·6666 . . ., the dots indicating that you may go on writing sixes for as long as you wish.

If you have not already done so, use your calculator to convert some everyday fractions into decimals, e.g. $\frac{3}{4}$, $\frac{4}{5}$, $\frac{7}{8}$, $\frac{5}{12}$.

Mixed numbers involve whole numbers and fractions; e.g. $2\frac{1}{4}$, $5\frac{3}{4}$. To evaluate these, work out the fraction first and then add the whole number. Take as an example $12\frac{5}{8}$; you work this out in the order $(5 \div 8) + 12$. Improper fractions are those where the numerator is larger than the denominator, e.g. $\frac{11}{8}$. These can be made into mixed numbers; $\frac{11}{8}$ can be expressed as $1\frac{3}{8}$. But it is not necessary to do this when using the calculator; simply divide 11 by 8.

Note this example:

Find $2\frac{5}{8}$ of 984

ALGEBRAIC		ARITHMETIC	
Key	*Display*	*Key*	*Display*
5	5	5	5
÷	5	÷	5
8	8	8	8
+	0·625	+=	0·625
2	2	2	2
×	2·625	+=	2·625
984	984	×	2·625
=	2583	984	984
		+=	2583

So conversion of fractions into decimals is easily achieved by use of the calculator. It is unlikely that you will need the opposite process, i.e. converting decimals to fractions. Decimals are so convenient to use and are the basis of both our currency and metric measure. However if it should be necessary to turn a decimal to a fraction, a calculator is not needed since it can be written down at once by a simple rule. An example might be when we wish to write 0·2345 as a fraction. Since the 2 represents tenths, the 3 hundredths, the 4 thousandths and the 5 ten-thousandths, the whole is 2345 ten-thousandths or $\frac{2345}{10000}$. Observe that the number of zeros in the denominator is the same as the total number of decimal places; this rule may be used to write down any decimal as a fraction. Examples:

$$0·856 = \frac{856}{1000} \qquad 0·97 = \frac{97}{100} \qquad 0·00387 = \frac{387}{100000}$$

Some examples to try

3a Convert to decimals $5\frac{2}{3}$, $3\frac{7}{20}$, $8\frac{11}{16}$, $15\frac{5}{12}$, $\frac{17}{8}$, $\frac{39}{12}$

3b Convert to fractions 0·311, 5·29, 0·037, 83·613

3c Find the value of each of the following:

$\frac{5}{8} \times 674$, $\quad 3\frac{5}{16} \times 866$, $\quad \frac{3}{11} \times 52·5$, $\quad 2\frac{7}{12} \times 90$

Finally, use your calculator to find two-thirds of 48, by expressing two-thirds as a decimal, then multiplying by 48.

Rounding up

Did you notice anything odd about the answer to the last example? If not, do it again before you read further. The answer will depend on your calculator, but at best you will get 31·999999 and possibly 31·999996. This may seem odd because one-third of 48 is 16, so two-thirds is 32. Use your calculator to work it out this way: enter 48, divide by 3, then multiply by 2. Your answer this time?

Two-thirds cannot be expressed as a decimal *exactly*. We get as a solution 0·66666 . . . . . as far as the capacity of the calculator. So if your calculator only works to eight digits and has an eight-digit display it will multiply 0·6666666 by 48 and obtain 31·999996. If it has an eight-digit display but works to more decimal places than eight it will probably give the answer 31·999999. Notice that even in this case we do not obtain 32 because however many sixes we take in 0·66666 . . . the result is always a little bit short of the true value.

Here is a very important point: *the calculator may not be absolutely accurate.* So treat answers with care; look at them before you copy them down. It is a good idea to make a mental check of each calculation before you enter it into the machine so that you know roughly what to expect as an answer. After all, there is the possibility that you may make a wrong entry and not notice it in the display. (See also Chapter 13 on this matter.)

The foregoing raises the idea of rounding of numbers. Take for example the two numbers 23 and 28, and suppose we wish to express these to the nearest ten. They both lie between 20 and 30 so it is one or the other, but which is the nearer? In the case of 23 it is nearer to 20 than 30, while 28 is nearer to 30 than it is to 20. This is called rounding a number to the nearest ten. 23 is rounded down to 20 and 28 is rounded up to 30. Where is the critical point at which rounding down changes to rounding up? Obviously it is the half-way mark, 25. In the case of 25, it doesn't really matter whether we round down or round up.

The same is true in the case of decimals. A number such as 2·3 rounded to the nearest whole number would be 2, but 2·8 would become 3. Similarly with a number such as 5·837 which is to be rounded to two decimal places we obtain 5·84. The second decimal place is 3, but we look at the next one and ask if it is over 5. In fact it is 7, so the original number is nearer to 4 than to 3 in the second decimal place. Hence 5·837 to two decimal places is rounded up to 5·84. As a final example consider 7·9182374 which might be obtained as a calculator answer. The answer to three decimal places is 7·918 and the answer to two decimal places is 7·92.

This is very important for calculator users. If you have an eight-digit display calculator and your answer involves more than eight digits, the extra figures are usually cut off and not rounded according to the above rule. For example, two-thirds would be expressed as 0·6666666, whereas (since the next figure is also a 6 and above the half-way mark) a more correct value would be 0·6666667. "More correct", be it noted, but not accurate.

Rounding of a number is important to the calculator user also when only part of the display is used. The most common example is when we are dealing with money and require answers to two decimal places only (i.e. pounds and pence). Suppose we are selling 3·7 metres of material at £4·58 per metre. Your calculator will give an answer 16·946 but this must be adjusted to the nearest penny, i.e. to two decimal places. Using the rule above the required answer is £16·95; in this case we round up. If the quantity had been 2·3 metres, the calculator answer would be 10·534 and to the nearest penny this would be £10·53.

Some calculators have a switch which makes them round numbers automatically. If the switch is set for two decimal places it gives an answer to two decimal places only, cutting off or rounding up as appropriate.

The existence of the ½p complicates matters a little. It is significant that banks ignore the ½p in their accountancy. If you wish to take these into account, the principle is the same. Notice that ½p is £0·005 and two "half-way marks" are now involved. Examples will illustrate. Consider £0·341 and £0·344. The half-way mark is £0·3425, so the first is expressed as £0·34 and the second as £0·345. The other half-way mark comes *above* the ½p. Take as examples £2·636 and £2·638. The half-way mark is £2·6375 so the first example becomes £2·635 and the second becomes £2·64.

Some further examples are given in this table:

An answer 5·8314 would be expressed as £5·83 or £5 83p
,, ,, 5·8322 ,, ,, ,, ,, £5·83 or £5 83p
,, ,, 5·8329 ,, ,, ,, ,, £5·835 or £5 83½p
,, ,, 5·834 ,, ,, ,, ,, £5·835 or £5 83½p
,, ,, 5·8362 ,, ,, ,, ,, £5·835 or £5 83½p
,, ,, 5·838 ,, ,, ,, ,, £5·84 or £5 84p

Percentages

Percentages are another way of expressing parts of a whole. In this case they are always expressed as parts per hundred. So 27 per cent means 27 parts out of a hundred. This could be expressed as a fraction $\frac{27}{100}$ or as a decimal 0·27. Conversion to fractions is not very important for the calculator user, but the ability to put percentages into decimal form is essential. This is explained in detail below.

Some calculators have a percentage key which enables the

user to obtain percentages automatically. The percentage of a certain quantity can be obtained or the quantity increased or decreased by a given percentage. The percentage key divides or multiplies by 100 automatically; once more see the instruction leaflet if your calculator has this key. However a percentage key is not necessary provided you understand how to express percentages as decimals.

To express percentages as decimals, remember that if you have a decimal number such as 0·12345, the first decimal place (1 in this case) indicates tenths, the second place (2 here) hundredths and so on. So taking the example above of 27 per cent, 27 hundredths would be written 0·27. This is the answer you would get if you divided 27 by 100 using your calculator. Sometimes we have a fraction of a percentage, e.g. $12\frac{1}{2}$ per cent. In such cases the easiest way is to express the percentage in decimal form first, so $12\frac{1}{2}$ per cent would be written 12·5 per cent. Either using your calculator to divide 12·5 by a hundred, or remembering the rule, we find that this would be 0·125 as a decimal.

Look at these examples:

54 per cent as a decimal is 0·54

2 per cent as a decimal is 0·02

70 per cent as a decimal is 0·70

$11\frac{1}{2}$ per cent as a decimal is 0·115

$3\frac{1}{4}$ per cent as a decimal is 0·0325

$33\frac{1}{3}$ per cent as a decimal is 0·3333 . . . .

100 per cent as a decimal is 1·00

125 per cent as a decimal is 1·25

$112\frac{1}{2}$ per cent as a decimal is 1·125

Some examples to try

3d. Express the following percentages as decimals: 30, 8, $22\frac{1}{2}$, 15, $6\frac{1}{4}$, 9·3, $66\frac{2}{3}$, 115, 104, 95.

Applying these principles to work out problems involving

percentages, suppose we require 15 per cent of £32·40. 15 per cent as a decimal is 0·15, so enter 0·15 in your calculator and multiply by 32·40. The answer is £4·86.

If you are still a little unhappy about changing the percentage to a decimal, you may do the whole calculation on your machine as follows: Enter 15, divide by 100, multiply by 32·40. In this case your first two operations express 15 per cent as a decimal and the third operation finds this part of 32·40.

Examples to try

3e. 18 per cent of 456

4 per cent of 625

8 per cent of 9·75

10 per cent of £8·40

5 per cent of £1·20

33⅓ per cent of £9·36

If you wish to find the same percentage of a number of items and your calculator has a constant key, the whole process is made much simpler. Suppose you wanted 15 per cent of 32, 56, 18 and 27. Enter 0·15 and press the K key. Now press 32 and ×. The answer is given immediately as 4·8. Press 56 and ×. Read answer 8·4. Press 18 and ×. Read answer 2·7. Press 27 and ×. Read answer 4·05. On some machines the constant facility can be combined with the percentage key, so that a constant percentage can be found of various numbers entered in turn.

Examples to try

3f. If V.A.T. is 8 per cent, find the V.A.T. on articles with the following prices:

£3·25   £4·60   £1·75   £0·63

Percentage added on or subtracted

In the practice examples above you were asked to find 8 per cent of £3·25. The answer was £0·26. This represents V.A.T. which has to be added on to £3·25 to make a total charge of £3·51. We may do this addition in our head or use the calculator, but we are doing two calculations: (1) finding the percentage and (2) adding it on. Unless we particularly require to know the actual V.A.T. we could find the final cost in one operation. The actual cost of the article, £3·25, is 100 per cent. To this is added 8 per cent, making a total of 108 per cent. So if we find 108 per cent of £3·25 we shall have the final cost without any further calculation. 108 per cent as a decimal is 1·08; enter this in your calculator. Now multiply by 3·25. The answer is £3·51.

Examples to try

3g. Add 12 per cent onto 325 (find 112 per cent of 325)

Add 65 per cent onto 428

Add 15 per cent onto £18

Add 6 per cent onto £15·50

Also repeat examples 3f finding directly the price with V.A.T. added.

If the percentage needs to be subtracted from the initial amount, as in the case of discount, the method is similar except that the percentage needs to be subtracted from 100 and not added as above. To return to our example of 8 per cent of £3·25, suppose this had to be deducted from £3·25. Since the initial cost represents 100 per cent and we are deducting 8 per cent, we are charging 92 per cent of the initial amount. So in this case enter 0·92 in the calculator and multiply by 3·25. The answer is £2·99.

Examples to try

3h. Try the four examples in 3g again, but this time deduct the percentage instead of adding it on.

A word of warning! Beware of calculations where percentages are added and/or subtracted successively and do not try to take short cuts! This type of example is where you may wish to add a certain percentage and then add or deduct a percentage of that total. Use your calculator to deal with each percentage increase (or decrease) separately and in turn. Here are two examples which you may care to work out on your calculator before you read further, where the examples are explained.

1. A manufacturer adds 10 per cent to the cost of making an article but his customer demands a discount of 10 per cent off the manufacturer's selling price. Does this mean that the manufacturer has no profit at all?

2. A manufacturer adds 5 per cent to the cost of an article to cover marketing and advertising costs and 20 per cent for his profit. His charge for an article costing £20 to manufacture is £25·20. Is this correct?

In example 1, take any figure as the cost of making the article. Let us say £50. In order to add 10 per cent we need to find 110 per cent of the cost. This gives the selling price and the amount the manufacturer receives will be 90 per cent of this selling price. Enter 50 into your calculator; multiply by 1·10; multiply next by 0·90. The answer is £49·50 – even worse for the manufacturer!

Work example 2 by entering 20 into your calculator, then multiply in turn by 1·05 and 1·20 to obtain the answer 25·20. This may be correct but did the manufacturer want to charge profit on marketing and advertising costs? If not then in this example he would have had to charge both the 5 per cent and the 20 per cent on his initial cost. In other words he would simply have added 25 per cent to the £20, giving a selling price of £25.

Proportional parts

Sometimes it is necessary to split an amount into given proportions. For example £3852 may have to be divided into three parts in the proportions 3:4:5. The basis of such calculations is to add the different proportions together (in this case $3 + 4 + 5 = 12$) and take the appropriate fraction of the initial amount, i.e. $\frac{3}{12}$, $\frac{4}{12}$, $\frac{5}{12}$. So it is required to find $\frac{3}{12} \times 3852$, etc. In each of the three necessary calculations 3852 is divided by 12. So start by working this out on your calculator (321) and use it as your constant. Obtain the answers by multiplying by 3, then 4, then 5. The parts are £963, £1284 and £1605.

Examples to try

3i. Divide £150 in the proportion 2:3:7.

A product is made by mixing certain materials in the proportions 1:3:4. What quantities of each should be taken to produce 220 Kilograms of the product?

Some complicated fractions

Earlier in this chapter fractions of a fairly straightforward type were covered. Sometimes however we meet fractions which have a calculation in either the numerator or denominator or both, for example $\dfrac{3 \cdot 8 \times 5 \cdot 7}{8 \cdot 6 + 4 \cdot 9}$

Examples of this type cause little difficulty if you have a calculator with a memory. The method is to work out the denominator (lower part) first and store it in the memory. Then work out the numerator and divide this result by that for the denominator contained in the store.

If your calculator does not have a memory it becomes a little more difficult but there are ways around the difficulties, especially if the calculator has a constant key. Some examples will illustrate the methods.

Firstly, take the fraction $\dfrac{64}{4 \times 8}$ where the denominator clearly comes to 32 and 32 divided into 64 gives an answer of 2. But this is exactly what we get if we first divide 64 by 4 and then divide the result by 8. Any problem which has only multiplication in the denominator may be worked in this manner. Try the following:

3j. $\dfrac{8 \cdot 3 + 5 \cdot 2}{5 \times 6 \cdot 4}$ (Method: add 8·3 and 5·2; divide the result by 5 and then divide that result by 6·4)

$\dfrac{6 \times (3 \cdot 4 + 5 \cdot 1)}{7 \cdot 8 \times 2 \cdot 5}$ (work out the addition in the brackets first; multiply the result by 6, then divide in turn by 7·8 and 2·5)

$\dfrac{14 \cdot 6 - 8 \cdot 2}{8 \times 2 \cdot 2 \times 5}$

The examples above have denominators which involve products only. Calculations of the type $\dfrac{60}{(2 + 3) \times 4}$ however call for the use of either a memory or a constant key in evaluation. Start with the denominator and find $2 + 3$; multiply the result by 4. This result has now to be divided *into* 60. Without a constant key or memory it is necessary to remember this result, clear the machine, enter 60 and divide by the earlier result. If your machine has a constant key, you simply press the constant key when you have worked out the denominator. Now enter 60 into the machine and divide by the constant. On a machine with a memory you can simply add the denominator to the memory (press M +) having calculated it, then enter 60 and divide by memory. (Press ÷ key followed by the RM or M out key, which returns the denominator to the display, and then the = or += key to obtain the answer.)

Examples

3k.
$$\frac{5\cdot8}{6\cdot4 \times (3\cdot6 + 2\cdot9)} \qquad \frac{12\cdot4}{(15\cdot2 - 7\cdot8) \times 36}$$

The ability to tackle even more complicated examples with the use of a constant key depends on how the key operates on your machine. If the constant key accepts a constant and holds it until the machine is cleared, then you may have to write down intermediate answers although use of reciprocal working (see below) can sometimes help. If the constant can be released you can tackle an example such as the one given at the start of this section $\dfrac{3\cdot8 \times 5\cdot7}{8\cdot6 + 4\cdot9}$

Proceed as follows: Add 8·6 and 4·9; press K; enter 3·8 and press division key; release K; press multiplication key, then 5·7; press equals key.

Another way of doing the same problem with the same type of machine is: Add 8·6 and 4·9; press K; press division sign key twice; release K; press multiplication key, then 3·8; press multiplication key, then 5·7; press equals key. In this case we have made use of the constant key to obtain the reciprocal of the denominator (see below and also Chapter 2). This gives 0·074074 and is the value of $\dfrac{1}{8\cdot6 + 4\cdot9}$. Finally we multiply this by 3·8 and 5·7. Notice that the reason you cannot do this unless your machine will release the constant in the middle of the calculation, is that when you try to multiply by 3·8, the machine will multiply by the constant factor, i.e. 13·5. Machines with a constant facility but no K key can also solve such problems via the reciprocal. Again care must be taken that the constant does not intrude upon the final multiplications.

Reciprocal working

You will remember explained at the end of the last chapter that a reciprocal of a number is unity divided by that number. The reciprocal of 6 is $\frac{1}{6}$, the reciprocal of 64 is $\frac{1}{64}$ and so on. Some calculators have a reciprocal key to give the reciprocal of a number automatically, but a constant key can obtain reciprocals just as easily. As an example of obtaining a reciprocal using a K key, the reciprocal of 64 is found as follows:

Enter 64 and press K.

Now press the division key.

(This divides 64 by your constant, which is also 64, so display now reads 1)

Press division key a second time.

(This divides 1 by the constant, 64)

The answer shown, 0·015625, is the reciprocal of 64.

Practice this process by finding the reciprocals of some common numbers such as 2, 8, 50, etc. Check your answers by multiplying them by the original number; in each case the final answer should be 1. Once again on machines without a K key if there is a constant division facility you will find you can arrive at reciprocals in a similar way.

The reciprocal can be of value when working out fractions. A fraction is inverted by taking its reciprocal as discussed towards the end of chapter 2. For example, the reciprocal of the fraction $\frac{3}{4}$ is $\frac{4}{3}$. You can check this on your calculator if you wish: $\frac{3}{4}$ is 0·75 and the reciprocal works out at 1·3333333 which is $\frac{4}{3}$ as a decimal.

The importance of this is that it is often easier to work out a complex fraction in its inverted form and then find the reciprocal of the result; this is particularly true if the fraction has addition and subtraction signs in the denominator but not in the numerator.

We had the example above $\dfrac{3·8 \times 5·7}{8·6 + 4·9}$. The difficulty is that the addition in the denominator must be worked out first, and then be divided *into* the numerator. However, it is easy to work out $\dfrac{8\cdot6 + 4\cdot9}{3\cdot8 \times 5\cdot7}$ by first adding $8\cdot6$ and $4\cdot9$, then dividing the result in turn by $3\cdot8$ and $5\cdot7$. The answer at this stage is $0\cdot6232686$ and if we now find the reciprocal of this, we invert the fraction so that it becomes the original one. Press the K key and then the division key twice. The final answer will be $1\cdot6044446$.

Some examples to try

31. $\dfrac{6\cdot3 \times 4\cdot7}{12\cdot4 - 5\cdot9}$ $\qquad\qquad$ $\dfrac{123 \times 61}{(87 + 79) \times 43}$

4

FIGURE FUN

A little light relief now! No doubt in all the work you have been doing with your calculator you have found a certain fascination in "number churning", i.e. having your calculator turn out numbers in various ways. Here are some interesting problems for you to try.

Sevens
Divide 1 by 7. Look at the first six decimal places. Now divide 2 by 7 and notice the first six decimal places again. Any comment? Next divide 3, 4, 5, 6 in turn by seven and look at your results.

If you have a calculator with a very large display (or means of obtaining a large number of decimal places) you will find other curious facts about these numbers. For example, 1 divided by 7 is 0·142857142857142857 . . . The six figures displayed in the first six decimal places are repeated as a whole indefinitely. This is a different type of recurring decimal to $\frac{1}{3}$ which gives 0·3333 . . . When other numbers are divided by 7 the same set of 6 decimal place figures will occur (with different starting points).

Pools win
A football match has three possible results: home win, away win, or draw. We will denote these respectively by 1, 2, and X. How many possible results are there for two football matches?

To answer this question, suppose the first match results in a home win, i.e. 1. There are three possible results for the second match, 1, 2, or X. In the same way there are three possible results if the first match has a 2 result, and again three possible results if the first match is a draw, X. So in all there are nine possible results of the two matches. These are all set out below for you to check:

11   12   1X   21   22   2X   X1   X2   XX

The next question is how many possible results are there if there are three matches? The nine possible results for two matches are given above and for each of these nine results the third match could produce a 1, 2 or X. So we could use the above results to produce a table which would start something like this:

111	121	1X1	211
112	122	1X2	212	and so on.
11X	12X	1XX	21X

Complete the table if you wish, but the important question is how many possible results are there? Since the third match produces three results for each of the earlier 9, there must be 3×9, i.e. 27 results. We now see a pattern beginning to emerge:

For 1 match there are 3 possible results

For 2 matches there are 9 possible results

For 3 matches there are 27 possible results

Each time we are multiplying by 3. So for 3 matches there are $3 \times 3 \times 3$ possible results. Those who are familiar with the idea of powers of a number will recognize this as 3^3, a short way of writing it. Continuing the pattern, if there are 4 matches there will be 3^4 results, i.e. $3 \times 3 \times 3 \times 3$. Clearly this comes to 81, but before long you are going to need your calculator.

How many possible results are there to 10 matches, and to 12 matches?

Some football pools require you to forecast the results of 10 or 12 matches and you can now work out the chances of winning such pools. You can find the number of possible results (let us call it N) and you know that there can be only one correct result, so the chance of winning is 1 in N.

Football teams

Talking of football, poses another interesting problem for your calculator and the result may give you a surprise!

With eleven players of a football team, in how many different ways can you arrange them in the positions on the field?

Take one position first, say goalkeeper. To fill this you have eleven possible players. Now take another position and you can fill this with any of the remaining ten players; the next position with any of the remaining nine and so on. For every one person you put in goal you have ten possible people for the second position, so you can fill these two places in 11 × 10 different ways. And for every one of *these* you can fill the third position in nine ways, so you can fill the three places in 11 × 10 × 9 different ways. And so it goes on. Hence the whole team can be arranged on the field in 11 × 10 × 9 × 8 × 7 × 6 × 5 × 4 × 3 × 2 × 1 ways.

(Note: a number such as this is called a *factorial*; the number given is factorial 11, often printed 11! Factorial 3 is 3 × 2 × 1, etc.)

Use your calculator to find the total number of team placings.

Discount diddle

A plumber of my acquaintance once asked me, "What per cent on is five per cent off?" Not quite certain what he meant by this I questioned him further and found that he wished to add a certain percentage to his bill so that when he allowed his customer 5 per cent discount for prompt payment, he would receive the initial amount!

Fortunately he had realized that if he added 5 per cent to the bill, deducting 5 per cent later would not result in his receiving the initial amount. Would he have had more or less? Try it on your calculator with a round figure such as £100. Remember that to add 5 per cent you multiply by 1·05 and to deduct 5 per cent you multiply by 0·95.

To work out the plumber's problem start with the supposition that the bill is for £100. To add on a quantity such as 5 per cent, we know that we multiply by 1·05, but with this problem we do not know the percentage he has to add on. Consequently we do not know the number to multiply by, so we can call it N. We know that we must multiply 100 by N, multiply this result by 0·95 and obtain an answer of 100. Writing this as an equation:

$$100 \times N \times 0·95 = 100$$

One doesn't have to be a mathematical wizard to look at this and realize that if you are going to multiply 100 by two quantities and still have 100, those two quantities must equal 1. So it follows that $N \times 0·95$ must equal 1. The only value for N which will give this is $\dfrac{1}{0·95}$, or in other words, the reciprocal of 0·95. Work this out on your calculator and you obtain 1·0526315. (It does not work out exactly).

You can test the accuracy of your result by multiplying 100 by this quantity and then by 0·95. Your answer should be 100. If fact you will find probably that your calculator gives you an answer of 99·999992; this corrected to two decimal places would be 100. So the actual percentage which the plumber needs to add on is 5·26315. This is not an easy amount to calculate without a calculator and my plumber friend was using a ready-reckoner. However $5\frac{1}{4}$ per cent (i.e. 5·25) is a fairly close approximation and if he added $5\frac{1}{4}$ per cent to his bill he would have the desired result to within a penny in £100.

Using your calculator, find what "percentage on" is 10 per cent off, and devise some simple examples for yourself.

5

USING THE MEMORY – IF YOU'VE GOT ONE!

Some electronic calculators – especially desk models – have a store or memory and sometimes two or more stores. The main value of this feature is the ability to hold the result of earlier calculation until it is required again. As far as actual calculation is concerned a machine with a memory will not do anything that the corresponding machine without a memory will do. But in the case of the latter it may be necessary to jot down on paper a particular answer in order to be able to use it later.

Take a simple example such as $\dfrac{12 + 27}{31 - 17}$. If your calculator does not have a memory you start by working out the denominator, $31 - 17$ and make a note of this result, 14. You now evaluate the numerator, $12 + 27$, then divide this by 14. If your calculator has a store, the method is exactly the same except that when you obtain the answer 14 you transfer this to the memory. Now evaluate the numerator and finally divide by the contents of the memory.

Basic operations with the memory
A calculator with a memory often has four main keys controlling the memory. Their operations and usual abbreviations are as follows:

M+   Add into memory
M−   Subtract from memory

RM (or M out)   Put contents of memory into display
CM   Clear memory

There is sometimes an accumulator key also. This enables results to be automatically added into the memory. If your calculator has different keys consult the instruction leaflet for the method of use.

The function of these keys may be illustrated by examples. You should be familiar by now with the operation of the four function keys, so these will not be set out but the memory keys will be indicated in brackets, e.g. (M+) to show the appropriate point in the calculation when they should be operated.

Example 1 $1 + 3 + 5 =$ (M+)
                $7 + 9 + 11 =$ (M+)
                $13 + 15 + 17 =$ (M+)
                $19 + 21 + 23 =$ (M+)   (RM)   (CM)

This little calculation has given you separate totals for the odd numbers, three at a time, the answers being 9, 27, 45, 63. Finally you obtained the sum of these four answers, 144.

Example 2
Evaluate $(32·4 \times 8·5) + (16·9 \times 12·4) - (72·6 \div 8·1)$
Proceed as follows:
                $32·4 \times 8·5 =$ (M+)
                $16·9 \times 12·4 =$ (M+)
                $72·6 \div 8·1 =$ (M−)   (RM)   (CM)

The final answer is 475·997. Note the manner in which we may add to or subtract from the memory.

Example 3
The contents of the memory may be used in any calculating process. We can multiply or divide directly by the contents

of the memory. Suppose we evaluate $\dfrac{46\cdot3 + 82\cdot9}{97\cdot5 - 12\cdot6}$, we would proceed:

$$97\cdot5 - 12\cdot6 = \qquad (M+)$$
$$46\cdot3 + 82\cdot9 =$$

Now press the divide key followed by (RM) and =.
The answer should be 1·5217903.

Example 4

It is possible to use the memory repeatedly in the same operation. An article is sold for £57·50 plus 10 per cent, less $2\frac{1}{2}$ per cent. The working is as follows:

$$57\cdot50 \qquad\qquad (M+)$$
$$\times\quad 0\cdot10 = \qquad (M+) \qquad (RM)$$
$$\times\quad 0\cdot025 = \qquad (M-) \qquad (RM) \qquad (CM)$$

The answer, to the nearest penny, will be £61·67. Notice that all the calculations are displayed so that one may write out the bill at the same time, as follows:

	£
Basic cost	57·50
Add 10%	5·75
	63·25
Less $2\frac{1}{2}$%	1·58
Total	61·67

Example 5

This type of example is met in commercial and statistical work. Suppose we are dealing with the output of a number of machines over a period of one week. The output of each may be displayed as follows:

	Machine 1	Machine 2	Machine 3	Machine 4	Machine 5
Monday	2·4	3·6	3·1	3·5	2·8
Tuesday	2·6	3·8	3·5	3·5	2·9
Wednesday	2·6	3·9	3·3	3·6	3·0
Thursday	2·5	3·7	3·4	3·6	3·0
Friday	2·5	3·7	3·2	3·5	2·9

Use your calculator to add each horizontal row, record the total at the end of the row and add it into the calculator memory. When you have completed the five rows, obtain the total in the memory and record this at the foot of your row totals. Now proceed similarly for each vertical column, setting down the result for each column and adding it into the memory. When you display the contents of the memory this time it should agree with your earlier total for all the rows. You now have a table which gives you total production on each day of the week, total production from each machine for the week and total production for the week from all the machines.

The accumulator key

Many calculators with a memory have an accumulator key which automatically adds into the memory the answer from each operation. If your machine has this feature, try it out as follows:

Press the accumulator key first

Now do $7 \times 9 =$

Next $8 \times 7 =$

Now press (RM) and obtain the answer 119 which is the sum of 63 and 56, the answers to your two products.

This accumulation feature can be very useful when compiling a bill of quantities, e.g. 12 at £2·35, 18 at £1·46, 14 at £3·50, 12 at £4·30, etc. The accumulator key is pressed first, then each price is worked out on the calculator and written onto the bill. When all the items have been calculated, the (RM) key is pressed and this gives the total cost, i.e. the amount to be entered at the foot of the bill. (See Chapter 6 for examples of this type).

Use of K and the Memory

In an earlier chapter it was pointed out that a constant factor, as operated by a K key, or by other means, was not the same as a memory. The former will allow repeated use of a number in a series of operations, e.g. multiplication, but can not store numbers while the calculator is being used to do other working. The difference between the two is well illustrated when we do an example requiring the use of both the constant factor and the memory.

Sometimes in mathematics we need to find the value of an algebraic expression when we are given the value of the unknown. Suppose the value of $5x^3 + 3x^2 - 7x + 1$ is required when $x = 4\cdot7$.

The method: On a machine with a K key you can enter $4\cdot7$ as the constant factor. Then enter 5, press the multiplication key three times and add the result to the memory. (Each time we press the multiplication key we are multiplying by x (i.e. $4\cdot7$), so after the first press we have $5 \times x$, after the second we have $5 \times x \times x$ and when we have pressed the key three times we have $5 \times x \times x \times x$ or $5x^3$.) You now enter 3 and press the multiplication key twice; this gives $3x^2$ and you add it to the memory. Enter 7 and press the multiplication key once to give $7x$, and subtract from the memory. Finally enter 1 and add to the memory. You can now display the contents of the memory as your required answer.

Key sequence: The operation of the keys with the accompanying display is given below:

Key	Display
4·7	4·7
K	4·7
5	5
×	23·5
×	110·45
×	519·115
M+	519·115
3	3
×	14·1
×	66·27
M+	66·27
7	7
×	32·9
M−	32·9
1	1
M+	1
RM	553·485

On machines with a constant multiplier but no K key, enter 4·7, press multiplication key, enter 5 and press equals key three times. This gives $5x^3$ which is added to memory. Clear display, and enter 4·7 again and find $3x^2$ in a similar manner, adding it to the memory. Proceed in a similar manner with the other terms. Notice that the constant has to be re-entered before each calculation.

The answer may be given as above or to one decimal place as 553·5 according to whether the value of x (4·7) is exact or not. Generally speaking when only one place of decimals is given in data, it is appropriate to give the answer to the same degree of accuracy only, i.e. one place of decimals. This matter is discussed in a later chapter (Chapter 13).

It may be interesting to note that it is possible to evaluate the above problem on a machine without a memory and without the necessity to write down intermediate answers. The method of doing this involves certain initial algebraic manipulation and details will be found in Chapter 16 on equations, under the heading "Nested multiplication".

Examples for you to try

5a. Find the value of the above expression $5x^3 + 3x^2 - 7x + 1$, when $x = 2·3$

Find the value of $3x^4 - 7x^3 + 8x + 12$ when $x = 4·36$

Find the value of $5x^3 - 6x^2 - 11x + 17$ when $x = 14$

Find the value of $6·2x^3 + 3·8x^2 - 5·2$ when $x = 8·3$

Practical tips for certain calculators

1. Some calculators do not have the M − key. Such machines usually have a "change sign" key which changes the sign of the display from positive to negative and vice versa. Hence to subtract the display from the memory, first change the sign of the display and then *add* to the memory.

2. Certain memory calculators do not have a separate "clear memory" key, the clearance being achieved by depressing the "display memory" key twice.

This can be awkward if the memory has been used during a calculation and it is then required to clear the number being held and store the present display in its place. To achieve this, press the keys in the following order: −, RM, =, M+; the memory now contains the required number.

The method used subtracts the number in the memory from the display. The display minus the memory number is now added to the memory number; the latter two cancel each other, leaving the required display in the memory. Remaining in the display is the earlier display number minus the memory. If the original display is required for further calculation it may be obtained from the memory by pressing RM.

6

MONEY CALCULATIONS

Probably the largest area of use for calculators is in commercial work, whether it be a large industrial firm or the shop around the corner. Although not all measurements have gone metric, increasing numbers are doing so and the fact that we now have a decimal currency in the U.K. also helps to do money calculations by machine.

The earlier chapters have given basic instructions in key operation and by now you should know how to operate your calculator in most circumstances. Key operating instructions, therefore, will no longer be given except in particular cases where special techniques are called for.

In the last chapter the bill of quantities was given as an instance where an accumulating memory can be of value. We may consider an example of this type to show how different machines would cope and what the user has to do.

The items of the bill may be as follows:

    12 at £2·35 each
    18 at £1·46 each
    14 at £3·50 each
    12 at £4·30 each
    13·4 metres at £5·46 per metre
    264 at £12·36 per hundred

The customer requires the items to be entered on his bill (or invoice), together with the cost of each set of items and the final total.

With the basic four-function calculator you work out each

line separately and write the total for that line on the bill, e.g. 12 at £2·35 = £28·20. The last two items need care because the calculator gives for the first 13·4 × 5·46 = 73·164. The pence must be rounded to 16½ (or to 16, if halfpence are being disregarded); the process has been explained in Chapter 3. When working out the last line it is advisable to consider 264 as 2·64 hundreds, so the calculation is really 2·64 at £12·36 each. The calculator gives £32·6304, which again has to be rounded to £32·63. When all the items have been entered on the paper, the calculator is used to add up the final column and give the total amount of the bill.

There are two refinements which more complex machines could employ. The first would be automatic rounding to two figures. Use of this switch would mean that we did not have to do our own rounding on the last two lines; but note that this switch would not help you if you wished to consider half-pence! The second is the accumulator key; operating this at the outset would mean that as each line is worked out, the result would be put into the memory automatically and when the six calculations had been completed, operation of the (RM) key would give the final total. This saves the trouble of entering the six items and adding them on the calculator to obtain the final total.

Many supermarket tills now calculate the change to be given for each bill. For example, the various items purchased may be listed, the total obtained (say £3·62) and the amount tendered by the customer (say £5) then recorded. The machine then states the amount of change to be given (£1·38 in this case). It is possible to do the same thing on your calculator. Add the following amounts, which may be items on a bill: £0·28, £0·54, £1·18, £0·60, £0·07, £0·36, £0·59. You will find that this totals to £3·62 as above. The customer now tenders you the £5 note, so from your total subtract 5. Your calculator will now register −1·38. So the change to be given is £1·38 (the minus sign indicates that you owe the customer this amount).

Examples of bills with several items to try

6a   56 at £3·18 each   6b   43 metres at £4·25 per metre
     29 at £2·46 each   87½ metres at £1·36 per metre
    115 at 34p each   5·3 metres at £17·54 per metre
     36 at £1·68 for ten   22 metres at £0·56 per metre

Tax and Discount

Profit, discount and Value Added Tax are usually expressed as percentages; discount is deducted from, the other two added to, the cost. Percentages have been dealt with in Chapter 3. Unless your calculator has a percentage key, the most important thing is to be able to express a percentage as a decimal, as was explained.

The required percentage of any given amount is obtained by expressing the percentage as an equivalent decimal and multiplying the amount by this.

Example Deduct 6½ per cent from a bill of £84·60.

$$\text{Amount} = £84·60$$
$$\text{Discount} = 0·065 \times 84·60 = £\,5·50$$
$$\text{Total} = £79·10$$

(N.B. that the calculator gives the discount as 5·499).

This calculation gives the actual discount in money to be written on the bill. Two calculations are involved: (1) finding the discount; (2) subtracting this from the amount. If only the final total is required this can be obtained directly as explained in Chapter 3. (Since £84·60 represents 100 per cent and we wish to deduct 6·5 per cent, the amount required will be

(100 − 6·5) per cent or 93·5 per cent. So £84·60 is multiplied by 0·935 and the result £79·10 obtained directly.)

Adding a percentage, such as V.A.T. is similar in the way that we may deal with it. The following example is done in two ways:

Add 8 per cent V.A.T. to an article costing £24·50

(i)
$$\begin{aligned} \text{Amount} &= £24\cdot50 \\ 8\% \text{ V.A.T.} = 0\cdot08 \times 24\cdot50 &= £1\cdot96 \\ \text{Total} &= £26\cdot46 \end{aligned}$$

(ii)
$$\begin{aligned} \text{Amount} &= £24\cdot50 \\ \text{Total} = 1\cdot08 \times 24\cdot50 &= £26\cdot46 \end{aligned}$$

Some examples to try

6c Deduct 5 per cent discount from an item priced at £8·40, then add 10 per cent tax onto this result.

6d The selling price of an article is £24·53 including V.A.T. at 10 per cent. A customer is allowed 5 per cent discount off the non-tax price. What does he pay? (Hint: the price with tax is 110 per cent, so the untaxed price is 100 per cent. Deduct 5 per cent from this and then add on the tax once more.)

6e The price of an article with 10 per cent tax added is £7·92. What is the price less tax?

Profit and loss

Profit and loss is another example of percentages applied to money calculations and the principles stated earlier apply equally. Loss may be regarded as negative profit, so we shall deal mainly with profit, remembering that while we add on a profit, we subtract a loss.

In mathematics we always regard percentage profit as being calculated on cost price. Thus an article bought for £1 and sold for £1·20 shows a profit of 20 pence. As a fraction of the cost price the profit is $\frac{20}{100}$ (i.e. 20p on 100p). To express this as a percentage we multiply by 100; the profit in this case is 20 per cent. So to calculate percentage profit on cost price we use the formula

$$\frac{\text{Profit}}{\text{Cost}} \times 100$$

Examples where we know the cost and wish to calculate a given profit are worked in exactly the same way as earlier examples on percentage. For instance if the cost is £2 and the percentage profit is 15 per cent, the actual profit will be 0·15 × £2. Should the selling price be required it is most easily calculated by remembering that it is 115 per cent of the cost price (the cost is 100 per cent of the cost and the profit is 15 per cent of the cost, so we add them together). Hence the selling price is 1·15 × £2, i.e. £2·30.

The reverse example (i.e. given the selling price and profit per cent, find the cost) may be regarded in the same way. If the selling price is £4 and the profit is 25 per cent of the cost, then the selling price is 125 per cent of the cost price. So if we wish to find the cost, we have to find 100 per cent knowing that 125 per cent is £4. In other words we require $\frac{100}{125}$ of the selling price. This is $\frac{100}{125}$ × £4, i.e. £3·20.

Examples to try

6f Find the profit per cent for (a) cost £72·50; profit £10
(b) cost £8·40; profit £1·50

6g Find the selling price for (a) cost £340; profit 22 per cent
(b) cost £7·30; profit 12 per cent

6h Find the cost price if (a) selling price = £155; profit = 20%
(b) selling price = £9·65; profit = 30%

Sometimes in commercial calculations the percentage profit is given on the selling price. This makes the problem entirely different. As an example, suppose I buy something for £1 and sell it for £2, the profit and the cost are both equal at £1. So my percentage profit, calculating it on the cost price as before, is 100 per cent. However, if I calculate the profit per cent on the *selling price*, the formula to use is now

$$\frac{\text{Profit}}{\text{Selling price}} \times 100,$$

and the profit is only 50 per cent of the selling price.

The oddest thing about this method of calculating profit per cent is that one can never have 100 per cent profit (unless the cost is nil). On the other hand a shopkeeper often knows the price of goods to the customer, whereas he would have to look up the price he paid, so it is more convenient to work profit on the selling price. As an example, booksellers know that the price of a paperback book is usually printed on the cover. To calculate a 35 per cent profit on the selling price, all they need to do is multiply the price printed by 0·35.

It is essential to note the two methods of calculation and to be quite certain when dealing with percentage profit that you know whether it is profit on the cost or on the selling price. If it is on the selling price, the percentage profit is worked out by use of the formula given in the previous paragraph. The other types of example are illustrated below:

(1) Selling price is £5·40, profit is 20 per cent of selling price, find the cost.
   The selling price is 100 per cent of the selling price and the profit 20 per cent of it.
   So the cost must be 80 per cent of the selling price. Hence cost = $\frac{80}{100} \times 5\cdot40$, or cost = $0\cdot8 \times 5\cdot40 = £4\cdot32$.

(2) Selling price £15, profit 18 per cent of selling price, find the profit.

Profit = 18 per cent of £15 = 0·18 × 15 = £2·70.

(3) Cost price £6·50, profit 18¾ per cent of selling price, find the selling price.

As in example (1), the cost price must be 81¼ per cent of the selling price. We require 100 per cent of the selling price.

So selling price $= \dfrac{100}{81\cdot 25} \times 6\cdot 50 = £8.$

Checking your bank statement

Errors can occur in statements issued by banks and it is advisable to check these. To explain the method the first few lines of a typical bank statement are given below.

		Debit	Credit	Balance
Jan 1	Balance brought forward			90·70
Jan 3	821364	13·05		77·65
Jan 6	821365	30·00		47·65
Jan 10	Sundries		57·14	104·79
Jan 11	821366	27·90		76·89
Jan 15	Sundries		217·30	294·19
Jan 16	821369	52·40		241·79
Jan 20	821368	9·35		232·44
Jan 21	821367	47·00		185·44
Jan 31	Balance carried forward			185·44

The first two columns give the date and the description (cheque nos., "Sundries", "Salary", etc.). The column headed *Debit* denotes payments out of the account, that headed *Credit* lists payments into the account, and the final column headed *Balance* gives the money still in the account after each transaction.

To check the account, begin by ensuring that the items are correct in the Debit and Credit columns; this you do by reference to your cheque book stubs and to your paying-in book. Items such as your salary may be paid directly into your account, but you should be able to verify that these are correct by reference to the statement from your employer. Similarly for other direct payments.

Now enter into your calculator the balance brought forward. Next take the items, line by line, in the Debit and Credit columns and enter these in your calculator, subtracing if in the Debit column and adding if in the Credit column. After each subtraction or addition the display in the machine should be identical with the balance shown. The final display should agree with Balance Carried Forward.

If your account is overdrawn after any particular item, this will be shown by a negative quantity in the display. It is often denoted on the bank statement by a letter D (for debit).

Example 6i. Check this bank statement:

		Debit	Credit	Balance
Mar 1	Balance Brought Forward			127·46
Mar 3	716224	46·13		81·33
Mar 5	716226	15·00		66·33
Mar 6	Sundries		32·40	98·73
Mar 10	Getwell Insurance Co.	16·50		82·23
Mar 11	716225	84·00		1·77D
Mar 15	Salary		197·40	195·63
Mar 18	716227	30·00		165·63
Mar 25	Sundries		18·05	181·68
Mar 27	716228	22·35		159·33
Mar 30	716229	5·27		154·06
Mar 31	Balance Carried Forward			154·06

Further calculations involving money will be found in the next two chapters.

7

INTEREST – SIMPLE AND COMPOUND

Interest paid on the loan of money to a bank, building society, etc. is another example of percentages applied to money calculations. By now you will have realized that all such calculations follow a similar pattern.

The percentage gain, whether it is interest, profit or anything else is obtained by putting the increase over the initial amount and multiplying by 100. As a formula we may write it as

$$\frac{\text{increase}}{\text{initial amount}} \times 100 = \text{percentage increase.}$$

In the last chapter, the increase was profit, the intial amount was the cost and the percentage increase was percentage profit. In the present instance simply read "interest" for "increase" and note that in the case of investment the initial amount is called the *principal*. So

$$\frac{\text{interest}}{\text{principal}} \times 100 = \text{percentage interest.}$$

Simple interest

Given the percentage interest rate, the calculation of the amount of interest in money involves another familiar pattern. We express the percentage as a decimal and multiply it by the initial amount, i.e. the principal. As a very simple example, suppose the principal was £100 and the percentage interest was 5 per cent. As a decimal 5 per cent is 0·05 and multiplying this by 100, we have the actual interest which is £5.

If we add the £5 interest to the principal of £100 we obtain what is usually called the *amount*, so the amount in this example is £105. If you refer back to the last chapter on profit you will note the similarities: principal corresponds to cost price, interest to profit and amount to selling price. Remembering this you should have little difficulty in dealing with an example which asks for the amount, given the principal and the interest per cent. Using the figures of the previous paragraph, the amount will be 105 per cent of the principal. We can express this as a decimal, 1·05, and multiply by the principal, £100. This gives the amount as £105, which is what we obtained above when we calculated the interest first and then added it to the principal.

So far the time of investment has not been mentioned. When we speak of 5 per cent interest, we usually mean 5 per cent per year. In other words, using the same example again, as long as our £100 is invested we shall receive £5 per year. Note, however, that this affects the amount because if £100 is invested for three years and you receive £5 per year, the amount at the end of three years will be £115. When we speak of receiving £5 per year we mean actually receiving it in the sense that it is paid to you. What happens if it is not paid to you yearly?

Compound interest

If the £5 interest earned is not paid but is added to the initial principal making £105, then this is what you have invested for the second year. So your capital for the second year is £105 and the interest of 5 per cent for the second year is on this figure and not on £100. This second year's interest comes to £5·25. This again is added to the money invested so that at the end of two years you will have £110·25. If this is left invested for one more year, then the interest is paid on £110·25 and comes to £5·51 for the third year. Hence at the end of the three years the amount is £115·76. If you compare this with the calculation for three years in the previous paragraph you will see that the amount in that case was only £115.

The type of interest which is paid each year is called *simple* interest, whereas the type we have just described in which the interest is re-invested to earn future interest itself, is called *compound* interest. Simple and compound interest will be illustrated further by the use of the calculator.

Examples

(1) Find 7½ per cent simple interest on the following investments:
   (a) £250 for 5 years
   (b) £830 for 4 years.
   7½ per cent interest is 0·075 as a decimal.
   Interest (a) is $250 \times 0.075 \times 5 = £93.75$
   Interest (b) is $830 \times 0.075 \times 4 = £249$

(2) Find the amount of £550 at 8 per cent simple interest (a) for one year and (b) for 6 years.
   8 per cent is 0·08 as a decimal and the amount after one year will be 1·08 times the principal.
   Amount (a) is $550 \times 1.08 = £594$.
   Note however that we cannot use this method in (b). Multiplying the answer for 1 year by six will not only multiply the interest by six but also the capital! We have to adopt the other method, i.e. calculate the interest for six years and then add it on to the capital.
   Interest for six years $= 550 \times 0.08 \times 6 = £264$.
   Amount after six years $= 550 + 264 = £814$.
   By calculator this is done continuously thus:
   $(550 \times 0.08 \times 6) + 550 = 814$.

(3) Find the amount of £550 at 8 per cent compound interest for 6 years.

We need to calculate the amount at the end of the first year which then becomes the principal for the second year. Using this we calculate the amount at the end of the second year which then becomes the principal for the third year and so on. Refer back to example 2 part (a) above.

The amount at the end of the first year is $550 \times 1 \cdot 08 =$ £594.

The amount at the end of the second year is $594 \times 1 \cdot 08 =$ £641·52. But the £594 was $550 \times 1 \cdot 08$ so the last calculation is really $550 \times 1 \cdot 08 \times 1 \cdot 08$ (Check it on your calculator if you have doubts). Similarly the amount at the end of 3 years will be $550 \times 1 \cdot 08 \times 1 \cdot 08 \times 1 \cdot 08$. A short way of writing this is $550 \times 1 \cdot 08^3$. By similar reasoning the amount at the end of 6 years will be $550 \times 1 \cdot 08^6$. Your calculator will give this answer as £872·78. (N.B. if your calculator has a constant factor key, K, enter $1 \cdot 08$ as your constant, then put 550 in the display and press the $\times$ key six times. Similarly if you have a constant facility operated other than by a K key.)

(4) Find the compound interest on £1250 at $8\frac{3}{4}$ per cent per annum for five years.

The amount after 5 years will be £ $(1250 \times 1 \cdot 0875^5) =$ £1901·32. Hence interest is $1901 \cdot 32 - 1250 = $ £651·32.

(5) Find how many years it takes an amount of money to double itself at $6\frac{1}{4}$ per cent compound interest.

Imagine the principal to be £100; we need to find how many years it takes for this to become equal to or just exceed £200. So we need to multiply 100 by $1 \cdot 0625$ repeatedly until the amount reaches or exceeds 200.

Using the constant key or other facility multiply $1 \cdot 0625$ by 100 repeatedly, counting the number of times to obtain an answer of 200 or just over 200. The answer is twelve, the amount after 12 years being £206·99.

Some examples for you to try

7a Find the simple interest on (i) £1540 at 8¼ per cent for five years, (ii) £85 at 8¼ per cent for three years.

7b Find the compound interest on (i) £860 at 7½ per cent for four years, (ii) £125·40 at 9 per cent for three years.

Using a formula

So far all examples have been worked by explaining the method from first principles; this way one understands what is being done. But at times in mathematics we have to do the same type of calculation repeatedly, the only difference being in the numbers involved, and at this stage working of the problem is often reduced to using a mathematical formula. The formula is obtained by putting letters instead of numbers and doing the working exactly as if the problem did contain numbers.

Taking an example from simple interest with £100 invested at 5 per cent for 7 years, the interest payable on one year will be £5 and in seven years will be £35. Similarly the interest on £100 at 8 per cent for four years will be £32. From this it should be clear that if £100 is invested, the simple interest is obtained by multiplying the rate by the number of years. Call the rate R per cent and suppose T (time) is the number of years, then the interest will be R multiplied by T, usually written RT.

But suppose it isn't £100 which is invested? Consider £1 first. If the interest on £100 for T years at R per cent is RT, then the interest for £1 will be one-hundredth part of that, or $\frac{RT}{100}$. What would it be if it was £5, £50, £500? Simply multiply

$\dfrac{RT}{100}$ by 5, 50 or 500 because it is just so many times what the interest is on £1. Finally suppose the principal is £P. In this case the interest will be $\dfrac{PRT}{100}$.

We have now obtained a mathematical formula for simple interest. If £P is invested for T years at R per cent per annum, then the simple interest, I, is given by the formula

$$I = \frac{PRT}{100}$$

To use the formula in your calculator to find the simple interest, enter the principal, P, multiply by the rate per cent, R, multiply by the number of yeats, T, and divide by 100.

One advantage of a formula is that it can be transposed. This means that it can be rearranged to obtain solutions when different quantities are given. Suppose for example that we know the simple interest, the number of years and the rate, and the principal is required.

Multiply each side of the formula $I = \dfrac{PRT}{100}$ by 100 and we obtain

$$100\,I = PRT$$

Write it the other way round

$$PRT = 100\,I \qquad\qquad (1)$$

Divide each side by RT to obtain

$$P = \frac{100\,I}{RT} \qquad\qquad (2)$$

In (1) divide each side by PT to obtain

$$R = \frac{100\,I}{PT} \qquad\qquad (3)$$

In a similar manner we could obtain

$$T = \frac{100\,I}{PR} \qquad\qquad (4)$$

So from the original formula we obtain three formulae, numbered (2), (3) and (4) above which, together with the original, enable us to solve any problem on simple interest. So if we required the principal which would earn £45 in 4 years at $7\frac{1}{2}$ per cent, we should use formula (2) which gives P in terms of the other three quantities. The method of using your calculator for this is to enter 100 and multiply by 45 (which is I in this case). Now divide by 7·5 (which is R) and then divide this result by 4 (the number of years). The answer is £150. (Notice the method of dividing 100 I by R and then dividing that result by T; this was explained in Chapter 3 on fractions).

Examples to try
Fill in the blanks in the following table for simple interest:

	Principal	Rate	Time	Interest
7c	£450	$7\frac{1}{2}\%$	5 yrs	
7d		8%	6 yrs	£130
7e	£320	$6\frac{1}{4}\%$	$4\frac{1}{2}$ yrs	
7f	£62·50		4 yrs	£12·50
7g	£1680	$9\frac{1}{2}\%$		£399
7h	£128		$3\frac{1}{2}$ yrs	£29·12

The formula for compound interest is a little more difficult. If P is the principal, A the amount (i.e. the principal together with the interest), R the rate per cent per annum and n the number of years, then $A = P(1 + \dfrac{R}{100})^n$. The formula is proved in Chapter 14. To use this formula, notice that $1 + \dfrac{R}{100}$ can easily be expressed as a decimal. Thus if the rate is 6 per cent, this is $1 + \dfrac{6}{100}$ or simply 1·06. Similarly 12 per cent gives a value of 1·12, 7½ per cent a value of 1·075 and so on. So if we require the amount which £750 will achieve at 5¾ per cent compound interest over 6 years, substitution in the formula gives A = 750 $(1 \cdot 0575)^6$. Notice that the power 6 applies only to the 1·0575 and not to the 750. So put 1·0575 in your calculator and by repeated multiplication find the value of $1 \cdot 0575^6$. The answer should be 1·3985636 and 750 is multiplied by this to obtain the amount, A, as 1048·9227. Expressing this in pounds and pence, the amount is £1048·92. If the interest only is required, £750 should be subtracted from this figure. If a machine with a constant key is being used it is easier to put 1·0575 as the constant, then put 750 in the display and press the multiplication key six times.

It is not easy to use the compound interest formula in a transposed form apart from $P = \dfrac{A}{(1 + \frac{R}{100})^n}$ which gives the principal that achieves a given amount at a given rate for a given number of years.

If it is required to find the number of years needed for a given principal to achieve a given amount at a given rate per cent, the best method of approach with a calculator is that given in example 5 on page 68. The method is to enter the $(1 + \dfrac{R}{100})$ as a common factor, then enter the principal and press the multiplication key repeatedly, counting the number of presses of the key, until the required amount is reached (or exceeded) as seen in the display. In the example immediately above where £750 was earning 5¾ per cent compound interest, if you wished to know how long it would take for the £750 to double itself, you would use 1·0575 as constant, enter 750, and multiply repeatedly until 1500 or more appeared in the display. This would be after 13 presses of the relative key, so the time would be 13 years. (The amount would then be £1551·34).

Some examples to try

(Other examples will be found under "Compound interest law" in Chapter 14).

7i Find the amount of (a) £425 at 5¾ per cent compound interest for 5 years (b) £630 at 7 per cent compound interest for 8 years.

7j Find the compound interest on (a) £88 at 9½ per cent for 4 years (b) £1265 at 8¼ per cent for 6 years.

7k Find the principal which would amount to £986·40 at 6½ per cent compound interest in 5 years.

7l How many years at 8 per cent compound interest would it take for £350 to amount to £699?

Interest compounded over short periods

So far only the case where the rate of interest was so much per cent per annum has been considered. Sometimes the interest is compounded over shorter periods. Be clear what this means. We are not saying that you invest £300 for only three months at 12 per cent per year. This would be quite simple: since the interest for a whole year would be £36, that for three months would be one-quarter of this, i.e. £9. What is meant by compounding over short periods is that while the money is loaned for a long period the interest is charged at a number of shorter periods. Thus we might find that £300 has been borrowed for two years at an interest rate of 9 per cent compounded quarterly, i.e. every three months.

To work out this problem, first find the annual rate (0·09) and divide it by 4 to get the quarterly rate (i.e. 0·0225). Use this as $\dfrac{R}{100}$ in the compound interest formula to find the amount A as follows:

$$A = 300\,(1\cdot0225)^8$$

Notice that although the time is two years only, the number of quarters is 8, so we put n = 8 in the formula. The answer is £358·45. This means that the interest paid is £58·45, whereas if the interest was 9 per cent compound annually, the interest would be £56·43. The difference becomes much greater when the interest is compounded at shorter intervals, e.g. monthly.

Exercises to try

7m Assuming compound interest at $7\frac{1}{2}$ per cent per annum, what sum of money should be invested now to provide a sum of £5000 in ten years' time. (Hint: since £5000 is the required amount, use the compound interest formula in the form which gives P, substitute and find P).

7n Find how long a sum of money takes to double itself at an annual rate of 6 per cent, compounded quarterly.

7o Find the difference between the interest on £100 at 6 per cent when it is compounded annually and when it is compounded monthly, for 4 years.

Regular investment

The idea of making regular payments to discharge a debt, e.g. weekly or monthly, has long been known and is employed in such things as H.P., mortgages, etc. These are dealt with in the next chapter. Various schemes of saving by regular payments are operated by the National Savings Movement, building societies, etc. as "save as you earn" schemes.

Calculation of interest in these cases is more difficult than the work already covered in this chapter, since the earlier work has been based on investment of a fixed sum (the principal). With this new situation, however, there is a continually increasing principal investment. The idea and the method of calculation are best explained by example:

£100 is invested annually at 8 per cent per annum compound interest for five years. What is the value of the investment at the end of that time?

The first £100 is invested for the full five years and at the end will amount to £100 $(1 \cdot 08)^5$, by use of the compound interest formula.

Similarly the second £100, which is invested for four years, will amount to £100 $(1 \cdot 08)^4$.

And so on for the others.

Hence the total amount at the end of the five year period will be

$100(1 \cdot 08)^5 + 100(1 \cdot 08)^4 + 100(1 \cdot 08)^3 + 100(1 \cdot 08)^2 + 100(1 \cdot 08)$ or £100 $(1 \cdot 08^5 + 1 \cdot 08^4 + 1 \cdot 08^3 + 1 \cdot 08^2 + 1 \cdot 08)$.

It is possible to work this out on the calculator as it stands, but reference to the later chapter on "Sequences and Series" (Chapter 14) will show that the quantities in the brackets of the last expression form a Geometrical Progression whose sum may be obtained by use of the formula given. The first term of the G.P. above is $1 \cdot 08$, the common ratio is $1 \cdot 08$ and there are five terms, so the sum is $\dfrac{1 \cdot 08(1 \cdot 08^5 - 1)}{1 \cdot 08 - 1}$

and the value of this is $6 \cdot 3359289$, so multiplying by a hundred and rounding the pence, the amount after five years will be £633·59.

However, regular savings are usually done on a monthly basis and not annually as above. In these cases the calculation is a little more difficult although the method employed above is incorporated in it. Again an example will illustrate:

Suppose £10 is invested each month for 5 years at 6 per cent per annum, what is the amount at the end of the period? The method will be explained first, then summarized so that it may be applied immediately to similar calculations by application of a formula.

Consider the first £10. In the first year it will earn 6 per cent of £10, i.e. £10 × (0·06)

The second £10 is only invested for 11 months (up to the end of the first year) so its interest will be $\frac{11}{12}$ ths that of the first £10, or £10 × (0·06) × $\frac{11}{12}$.

We may proceed in this way to find the interest earned during the first year of all the other £10's invested in that year and then add them to obtain the total interest earned in the first year. This will be (in £s)

$$10(0·06) + 10(0·06) × \frac{11}{12} + 10(0·06) × \frac{10}{12} + \ldots$$
$$\ldots + 10(0·06) × \frac{1}{12}$$

or $10(0·06) (1 + \frac{11}{12} + \frac{10}{12} + \frac{9}{12} + \ldots \ldots + \frac{1}{12})$

The sum of the fractions in the last bracket is $\frac{78}{12}$ or 6·5 (treat 1 as $\frac{12}{12}$), so the interest earned is £10(0·06)(6·5).

In addition, the total amount deposited in the first year at £10 per month is £120.

So at the end of the first year the amount (i.e. capital sum interest earned) is £120 + £10(0·06)(6·5) or £123·90.

The investments made during the second year may be considered in exactly the same way and the amount at the end of the second year (from capital invested in the second year only) will also be £123·90. The same is true of the third, fourth and fifth years.

At the end of each year, therefore, £123·90 from that year is left to be invested for the remainder of the five years. The compound interest formula is $P(1 + \dfrac{R}{100})^n$, hence:

The first £123·90 in four years will amount to £123·90(1·06)⁴. The second, third and fourth £123·90 will amount to, respectively, £123·90(1·06)³, £123·90(1·06)², £123·90(1·06). The fifth £123·90 will have been accumulated only at the end of the five years and will amount to £123·90 only.

By addition, the total sum at the end of five years will be £123·90(1 + 1·06 + 1·06² + 1·06³ + 1·06⁴).

The numbers in the brackets form a geometrical progression with first term 1 and common ratio 1·06, so the sum (see Chapter 14) will be

$$\frac{1·06^5 - 1}{1·06 - 1}$$

and the total amount will be

$$£\frac{123·90(1·06^5 - 1)}{0·06}$$

Working this out on the calculator the answer (to the nearest penny) is £698·44.

The above working may now be summarized into a formula which, by substitution, will give the amount after a number of years of a regular sum invested monthly.

Suppose the sum invested per month is £P

The number of years is n

r is the rate per cent expressed as a decimal (e.g. 6 per cent is 0·06, 10 per cent is 0·10, 4½ per cent is 0·045)

The amount will be

$$\frac{P}{r}(12 + 6·5r)[(1 + r)^n - 1]$$

If the investment is *annually* and not monthly (as in the first example above), omit the first bracket, so that amount =

$$\frac{P}{r}[(1 + r)^n - 1]$$

You may test the correctness of these formulae by using the values from the worked examples above. If your calculator has not got a memory start by working out the first bracket, make a note of the answer and then proceed as follows:

Evaluate $(1 + r)^n$

Subtract 1

Multiply by the value of the first bracket (already found)

Multiply by P

Divide by r.

As a further example of the use of the formula we may check an advertisement for a "Save as you earn" scheme which said that the rate of interest was $8\frac{3}{4}$ per cent per annum and that after investing £10 per month for five years you would receive £748.

In this case P is 10, r is 0·0875, n is 5.

Substituting, the amount will be

$$\frac{10}{0.0875} \quad (12 + 6.5 \times 0.0875) (1.0875^5 - 1)$$

The method of working is as follows (at point A record the result either by adding into the memory or by writing down the answer if your machine does not have a memory):

6.5×0.0875	=	0·56875
$+ 12$	=	12·56875 (A)
1.0875^5 (use constant key)	=	1·5210598
$- 1$	=	0·5210598
$\times 12.56875$ (from A)	=	6·5490703
$\times 10$	=	65·490703
$\div 0.0875$	=	748·46517

The answer confirms the claim of the advertisement.

Examples to try

7p Check these figures given by a building society for the amounts achieved by regular monthly subscriptions with an interest rate of 9 per cent per annum.

Monthly subscription	1 year	2 years	3 years
£2	25·17	52·59	82·44
£5	62·93	131·44	206·16
£8	100·68	210·36	329·94
£10	125·85	262·95	412·38
£30	377·55	789·03	1237·59

8

BORROWING MONEY

In the last chapter, simple and compound interest were considered from the point of view of the lender or depositor in a bank, etc. Naturally the same rules apply in the case of borrowing money. If a person deposits £100 in a bank at 8 per cent simple interest, he receives £8 at the end of each year. If a person *borrows* £100 from a bank at 8 per cent simple interest, he *pays* £8 at the end of each year. So where there is a straightforward loan of a lump sum to a person which he will repay at the end of the loan period, the calculations are exactly as set out in the previous chapter.

Loans
The type of loan being considered above is where an amount of money is lent for a specified period at the end of which it is repaid in full. Calculation of interest in such a case depends on whether the interest is simple or compound. If interest only, excluding loan repayment, has to be paid at regular intervals throughout the period of the loan this is simple interest and the formula given in the last chapter will apply. This is

$$\text{Interest} = \frac{\text{Amount loaned} \times \text{Years} \times \text{Rate}}{100}$$

In the previous chapter, P was used for the principal which is the same as the "amount loaned" above. Remembering this, there were several versions given of the formula in order to calculate different quantities, e.g. rate, years.

If the interest on the loan is not paid until the loan itself is repaid at the end of the loan period, then the interest should be calculated by the compound formula, since after the first year the value of the money on loan has increased by virtue of the interest it has earned in that year. In this case also, the formula given in the previous chapter applies. This is $A = P(1 + \frac{R}{100})^n$ where – in this instance – A is the total repayment (i.e. amount of loan + interest), P is the money loaned initially, R is the rate per cent per annum and n the number of years.

Two examples will illustrate the method of use.

(1) £500 is borrowed for 3 years at 12 per cent, the interest to be paid at the end of each year; what is the cost of the loan?

The total interest $= \frac{500 \times 3 \times 12}{100} = £180$. This is the total cost of the loan and means that at the end of the first year £60 interest is paid, at the end of the second year a further £60 interest, and at the end of the third year £560 is paid, made up of £60 interest and the £500 loan repayment.

(2) £1500 is borrowed for 4 years at 12 per cent per annum compound interest; what is the total cost of the loan?

$$\text{The amount repayable at the end} = 1500(1 + \frac{12}{100})^4$$
$$= 1500(1 \cdot 12)^4$$
$$= £2360 \text{ (to nearest } £1)$$

Hence the cost of the loan is £860.

Sometimes we wish to know the rate of interest which we are being called upon to pay. This is easy to find where the interest is calculated as simple interest. We should use the formula in the form $R = \frac{100\,I}{PT}$. In the case of compound interest the calculation is much more difficult to do with a simple calculator since the working out involves finding the multiple root of a number, i.e. a number which when multiplied by itself a number of times gives a desired quantity. The best one can do is to make various "guesses" and calculations until an approximate solution is reached. An example will illustrate.

A loan of £500 for 5 years requires a repayment of £881 at the end of the time; what rate is being charged?

Using the compound interest formula $A = P(1 + \frac{R}{100})^n$

$$881 = 500(1 + \frac{R}{100})^5$$

This may be expressed as

$$(1 + \frac{R}{100})^5 = \frac{881}{500}$$

$$\text{or} \quad (1 + \frac{R}{100})^5 = 1 \cdot 762$$

We could find $1 + \frac{R}{100}$ if we were able to find the fifth root of $1 \cdot 762$, but this is difficult with a simple calculator. It is far easier to take some possible values of R and work out powers of $1 + \frac{R}{100}$ until we obtain a value of $1 \cdot 762$ or thereabouts. Making a first guess that R may be 10, we calculate $1 \cdot 10^5$ to obtain $1 \cdot 6105100$. This is less than the required value, so try $R = 11$, i.e. find $1 \cdot 11^5$. This time the answer is $1 \cdot 6850581$, which is nearer. However $1 \cdot 12^5$ gives $1 \cdot 7623416$, which is very close to the required value, so the interest being charged is 12 per cent.

Examples to try

8a What is the cost of borrowing £850 for three years at $11\frac{1}{2}$ per cent compound interest?

8b A loan of £600 for three years costs £289. What is the rate
of compound interest per annum?

Regular repayment of loans

Loans are often repaid by regular payments over a period,
e.g. monthly for three years. Examples are mortgages and hire
purchase. In such cases a building society or finance house
provides the money for you to have certain goods and you
undertake to repay them by regular instalments for the loan
which bought those goods.

Certain formulae are now given which will enable you to
make various calculations relating to loans and these will all
be illustrated. Working out the cost of the loan when we are
given the amount borrowed and the amount actually paid need
not concern us here since this is a straightforward calculation of
total payments (i.e. amount of each payment × number of
payments) less the amount borrowed.

$$(1) \qquad \text{Annual payments} = \frac{Lr(1 + r)^n}{(1 + r)^n - 1}$$

In the formula L is the amount of the initial loan in £'s, n is
the number of years and r is the rate per cent compound
interest per annum expressed as a decimal (i.e. 6 per cent is
0·06, 12½ per cent is 0·125, etc.). Notice that the interest is
compound and the repayments are equal annual payments.
After n payments the loan and interest is paid off.

As an example, £300 is borrowed at 12½ per cent compound
interest to be repaid by four equal annual instalments.

In this case, L is 300, r is 0·125 and n = 4. 1 + r will be
1·125.

So the annual repayments will be $\dfrac{300 \times 0·125 \times (1·125)^4}{(1·125)^4 - 1}$

Start by working out 1·125⁴ and store in the memory or record
on paper; the answer is 1·6018066. Next work out the numer-

ator and divide this by 0.6018066. The annual instalments are £99·81. If we wished to know the total cost of the loan, the cost of one instalment is multiplied by four and the £300 deducted. The cost is £99·24.

The formula given above may be transposed in order to obtain other information. Two such arrangements are:

$$(2) \qquad L = I \times \frac{(1 + r)^n - 1}{r(1 + r)^n}$$

where I is the annual instalment in £'s. This formula gives the amount of the initial loan if the instalments, the rate and the number of years are known.

$$(3) \qquad (1 + r)^n = \frac{I}{I - Lr}$$

This formula gives the number of years when the other items are known. The method of use may be illustrated by taking the example above where $L = 300$, $r = 0.125$, $I = 99.81$ and we wish to find n.

The right-hand side of formula (3) becomes

$$\frac{99 \cdot 81}{99 \cdot 81 - 300 \times 0 \cdot 125}$$

which equals 1.6018295.

In this example $1 + r$ is 1.125. This should now be entered in the calculator as a constant and the multiplication key pressed until the value of 1.6018295 is reached (or very close). We find that 1.125^4 gives 1.6018066 which agrees with the desired result to four decimal places, so the time required to complete the repayment is 4 years.

As an example of the use of formula (2) above, we could find the initial loan when asked to pay £120 per year for five years with interest at 11 per cent compound. Substituting in the formula:

$$L = 120 \times \frac{1 \cdot 11^5 - 1}{0 \cdot 11 \times 1 \cdot 11^5}$$

Start by finding $1 \cdot 11^5 = 1 \cdot 6850581$, substitute this value above and work out the rest of the calculation. The answer is that the initial loan was £443·50.

Examples to try

8c Find the annual repayments for a loan of £1000 at $11\frac{1}{2}$ per cent compound interest, repayable in five equal annual instalments.

8d. Find how long it would take to repay the loan in 8c if the annual repayments were £150.

8e When interest is being charged at 11 per cent compound, how much can I borrow if I am prepared to make repayments of £200 per year over four years?

Mortgages

If money is borrowed to buy a house it is usually called a mortgage and most mortgages are arranged through building societies. Those arranged through other organizations work in very much the same way. The essential feature is that money is loaned and the borrower repays the loan by regular payments. Usually these payments are arranged on a monthly basis and this makes calculation a little more difficult. The source of the difficulty will be realized when it is remembered that mortgages extend over something like twenty years so that over 200 payments are involved. These payments are all of equal value but every one is different in the proportions of it which go to paying interest and to paying off the loan. At the commencement of the mortgage, repayments are largely in payment of interest while towards the end of the mortgage period each payment is almost all repayment of capital with very little interest paid.

Building societies and others who have to do these calculations use computers or books of tables to obtain the results.

However it is possible to get a very close result (to within a few pence) by using a calculator. The method is based on the formula given in the previous section.

If the mortgage is to be repaid by *annual* instalments the formula to use is:

$$\text{Annual payment} = \frac{Lr(1 + r)^n}{(1 + r)^n - 1}$$

If the repayments are to be *monthly* (as is usually the case), work out an annual payment by use of the above formula and divide the annual payment by $12 \cdot 2$.

An example will illustrate. A building society is charging 11 per cent interest on mortgages and for a mortgage of £10,000 requires monthly repayments of £103·22 over 20 years. Check these figures.

Using the formula, the right-hand side becomes

$$\frac{10,000 \times 0 \cdot 11(1 \cdot 11)^{20}}{1 \cdot 11^{20} - 1}$$

To work this out by calculator, find $1 \cdot 11^{20}$ first ($8 \cdot 0623095$). If your machine does not have a memory, write this down and use in working out the rest of the problem. If your calculator has a memory proceed as follows:

> From the answer subtract 1.
> Add result to memory.
> Add 1 to display.
> Multiply by 10000, then by 0·11.
> Divide by memory.

At this stage the answer should be that the annual repayment is £1255·76. If this is divided by 12·2 the anwer is £102·93 which is 29p away from the correct answer.

To get a more accurate answer would require considerable working. The figure of 12·2 is not accurate and varies with the number of years of the mortgage and with the rate of interest.

A very rough figure for the repayments could be obtained simply by dividing the annual payment into twelve equal instalments. However, this would not take into account the reduction of interest to be paid, by repayments during the year.

Examples to try

The following Building Society figures for monthly repayments may be checked:

8f Loan £3000; rate 11 per cent; repayment over 15 years; monthly payment £34·10

8g Loan £5000; rate 11 per cent; repayment over 25 years; monthly payment £49·01.

8h Loan £10,000; rate 7·40 per cent; repayment over 15 years; monthly payment £92·15.

8i Loan £5000; rate 7·40 per cent; repayment over 20 years; monthly payment £39·97.

Hire purchase

Hire purchase is another example of money being borrowed (this time to buy specific goods) and the loan being repaid with interest by regular payments made over a period of time. With hire purchase the payments are either monthly or weekly. The percentage rate of interest is seldom given on the price tags, so this type of calculation is hardly applicable for the general user. It is easier and more appropriate to find the actual cost of the loan in terms of money. Enter into the calculator the amount of the instalments and multiply by the number of instalments; then add any intiial deposit which has to be paid. The cost of the loan is then found by subtracting from this total the cash price of the article being bought.

Example

Weekly instalments payable 67p for 2 years (i.e. 104 weeks)

$$= 0·67 × 104 \qquad = £69·68$$

Initial deposit $\qquad = £5·50$

$£75·18$

Cash price $\qquad = £62·50$

Cost of loan $\qquad = £12·68$

When considering the cost of buying by hire purchase it may be worthwhile to remember that often the marked selling price of an article is reduced if it is bought for cash. A truer picture of the cost of the loan is obtained by using that discounted price.

The matter of whether to buy by hire purchase or to wait until one has enough money to pay cash is an individual choice; it is very difficult to make any objective judgement of which method is preferable. You are clearly going to pay more in the former case but you have the earlier use of the article.

The other question for individual judgement is how much one can afford to pay out regularly on hire purchase instalments. There is another use for the calculator here in balancing your budget of income and expenditure. Total your regular expenditure on food, clothing, light and heating, housing (mortgage, rent, rates), etc. and subtract this from the amount of your take-home pay. This should give a clear indication of what commitments you can afford to enter into.

Credit cards

Credit cards are issued to customers by banks and other organizations so that the customer does not have to pay cash for items which he buys. Instead he gives the number of the credit card and the shopkeeper uses this to claim payment from the customer's account with the issuing authority, e.g. a bank.

There are different methods by which the bank reclaims this money. The customer may authorize payment from his account (or send a cheque) and there usually is no charge if this is within a specified period, or he may undertake to repay the amount over a longer period. In the latter case a fixed percentage has to be repaid each month and interest is charged on the outstanding balance. This interest is usually around 2 per cent per month. The calculation of the actual annual interest rate is difficult because of the repayments, but although 2 per cent seems small, reference to the section on "Interest compounded over short periods" in the last chapter will show that this monthly rate amounts to quite a large yearly rate.

Since the interest is compounded monthly, the annual rate is found in the same way as compound interest. Assuming a rate of 2 per cent per month, enter $1 \cdot 02$ into your calculator and (using the constant facility if available) multiply by $1 \cdot 02$ eleven times, i.e. find the value of $1 \cdot 02^{12}$. This comes to $1 \cdot 2682413$, so that the annual rate of interest is over $26 \cdot 8$ per cent, and this is the annual rate being paid on any money owed.

9

CONVERSIONS, METRIC MEASURE

The great advantage of the decimal system is that it always counts in tens. The decimalization of British money showed the advantage of such a system applied to commercial calculations. The increasing change-over to the metric system of weights and measures will further simplify such work.

The metric system

As with decimal currency, calculations involving metric units are simple operations with decimal numbers, the easiest of which can be worked mentally and the rest quickly done on a calculator.

In a period of change from a non-decimal to a decimal system difficulties can arise since people are not familiar with the measures. A person who is used to buying food in kilogrammes knows how much bulk to expect in one kilogramme; a person who has always bought food in pounds weight may be quite uncertain. Worse still, if something costs 35p per lb., is it dear, cheap or about the same price when marked at 75p for a kilogramme?

It is for this reason that we have to do conversions which change units from one system to another. Unfortunately the factors which have to be employed are not simple; many are only approximate if we express them to six decimal places! For this reason your calculator is going to be of great value. The principle of conversion is easy when the factor to multiply by is known. We obtain this information from conversion tables.

A table of conversion factors is given at the end of this chapter and they cover most common uses. They are given to eight-figure accuracy but, as explained later, for most purposes the first four (or even two) figures will give acceptable results. Certain experts may require factors other than those given but these are obtainable from specialist sources. The first four sections of the tables appearing at the end of this chapter cover length, area, volume and weight; the next section is for liquid capacity and in addition to the more usual litres, pints, etc., includes millilitres and fluid ounces in which medicines are or were measured; the final section covers conversion from volume (metric) to capacity (Imperial) and volume (Imperial) to capacity (metric).

Using the tables

At the head of the columns are the words *From*, *To* and *Multiply by* and these words should be read immediately before the corresponding measure or factor on each line. Thus the first line will read: From centimetres to inches, multiply by 0·3937008. So that if 25 centimetres was required in inches, we would multiply 25 by 0·3937008 (answer 9·84252).

The lines of the tables are arranged in pairs where the second line is the reverse of the first, e.g. the first line of the table gives centimetres to inches and the second line gives inches to centimetres. There is an obvious relationship between the numbers given on each pair of lines, since one will be the reciprocal of the other. To illustrate this in a simple way, if there are 3 feet in 1 yard, there must be $\frac{1}{3}$ yards in one foot. This relationship means that, if desired, the table could be made only half its present length. If we then wished to do the conversion on the second line of a pair as at present, we should use the factor on the first line, but divide by it instead of multiply by it. Illustrating with feet and yards once more, to change 6 yards to feet, multiply by 3 to obtain 18; to change 24 feet to yards, divide by 3 to obtain 8 as the answer.

Illustrating this from the conversion tables, above we converted 25 centimetres to inches by multiplying by 0·3937008. Suppose we now wished to express 14 inches in centimetres. The factor given in the second line of the table in order to convert inches to centimetres is 2·5399999. So 14 inches = 14 × 2·5399999 = 35·56 centimetres (to two decimal places). However we could have done the calculation by *dividing* 14 by the factor 0·3937008 from the line above. Then 14 inches = 14 ÷ 0·3937008 = 35·56 centimetres.

Notice that the answers above were given to two decimal places only although the factors given and the answer shown in the display contain more than two decimal places. We are dealing with measures and for everyday purposes we seldom need, or are able, to measure centimetres to anything like two decimal places. This would require measurement to one-tenth of a millimetre! More decimal places would require even greater accuracy of measurement. Because of this, it will probably serve most purposes if only the first few figures (say four) of the constants in the tables are used.

Two more worked examples are given below (in this case using only four or five figures from the tables:

7 lb. weight = 7 × 0·4536 = 3·18 kilogrammes (to 2 dec. places)

18 litres = 18 × 1·7598 = 31·68 pints (to 2 dec. places)

Examples to try

9a Convert (i) 57 metres to yards

           (ii) 22 yards to metres

           (iii) 35·4 kilometres to miles

           (iv) 40 miles per hour to kilometres per hour

9b Convert (i) 8 ounces to grammes
           (ii) 14 pounds to kilogrammes
           (iii) 4 gallons to litres
           (iv) 1 acre (i.e. 4840 square yards) to square
                metres.

Cost conversions

The work so far has been simple conversion of measure from
one system of units to another. But often we need to compare
the cost of materials when the prices quoted are for different
units, and this is particularly true in a period of change from
one system of units to another. When we have been familiar
with costs of materials by the yard, by the pound weight or by
the pint, we are somewhat at a loss when we find costs given
for a metre, kilogramme or a litre. How are these problems
tackled on the calculator?

Taking a line from the conversion tables as an example, to
convert kilogrammes to pounds we multiply by 2·205 (using
four figures only). This is another way of saying that there are
2·205 pounds in a kilogramme. If something costs 50p per
kilogramme, the cost per pound would be 50 ÷ 2·205 = 22½p.
So for this type of problem we use the conversion tables but
divide the cost by the factor given.

Here are further examples:

1. What is the cost per yard if material costs £2·35 per metre?
   The conversion from metres to yards is given as 1·0936133.
   Divide 2·35 by this and correct the answer to two decimal
   places. The cost is £2·15. To illustrate the point about
   using only four figures of the conversion factor, note that
   if you do so you get the same answer of £2·15, whereas
   if you use only three figures (i.e. 1·09) the answer is one
   penny out!

2. If a product costs 45p per lb. weight, what is the cost per
   kilogramme?

Divide £0·45 by the conversion factor 0·4536 to obtain the equivalent price of £0·99.

3. I am willing to pay up to £8 per square yard for a certain covering material, but the salesman says it is now sold by the square metre; what is my limit price per square metre? Square yards to square metres has a conversion factor of 0·8361 and dividing 8 by this, my price limit is now £9·57.

Examples to try

9c If petrol is 76p per gallon, what is the price per litre?

9d Fruit is marked at 45p per kilogramme; how much is this per pound?

9e A transport cost is 6·8p per mile. What is this per kilometre?

9f If certain material costs £1·22 per lb. weight, what is the cost per kilogramme?

Foreign currency conversions

A conversion that is particularly important when going abroad is the change from one currency to another. With a calculator this type of conversion is straightforward and is illustrated below by examples. It is essential to know the current exchange rate when making such calculations. Note also that banks or agents exchanging money make a small charge for their services and this is deducted from the amount paid to you so that you may not get exactly the amount you calculate. The deduction varies from one country to another and sometimes within a country, so no rule can be given. However, this will always be explained when exchanging money, if requested.

1. I wish to change £35 into French francs when the exchange rate is 10·94 francs to the £1. What will I receive?
Since £1 is exchanged for 10·94 francs, £35 will produce

35 times this amount, i.e. 382·90 francs. (Less any deduction for bank charges.)

2. While in France with the above exchange rate, I see an article priced at 240 francs; what is its equivalent price in sterling?

Since there are 10·94 francs to the £1 divide 240 by this to obtain the equivalent price of £21·94.

3. When the exchange rate is 2·53 German marks to the American dollar, how many marks do I get for 350 dollars? Number of marks is 350 × 2·53 = 885·50.

4. What is the equivalent of 2200 Spanish pesetas (a) in Italian lira (b) in Dutch guilder? (Exchange rates: 11·36 lira to 1 peseta; 22·18 pesetas to 1 guilder.)

2200 pesetas = 2200 × 11·36 lira = 24992 lira.
2200 pesetas = 2200 ÷ 22·18 guilder = 99·19 guilder.

Examples to try

9g Using the exchange rates above convert the following:
 (i) £135 into French francs.
 (ii) 350 German marks into American dollars.
 (iii) 22000 lira into pesetas.
 (iv) 5500 pesetas into lira.

9h Using the exchange rates above, what is the value of the Italian lira in terms of the Dutch guilder?

9i If petrol costs 76p per gallon, what is the cost in francs per litre to which this is equivalent when the exchange rate is as above? (Hint: refer back to 9c above).

Temperature conversions

In Britain we have used both Farenheit and Centigrade temperature scales for some time, but the move is now towards standardization on the Centigrade scale (also known as the Celsius scale).

The conversion is a little complicated since the size of a degree on the Fahrenheit scale (denoted by °F) is smaller than on the Centigrade scale (denoted by °C) and freezing point on the two scales differs, i.e. 32°F and 0°C. It is necessary to use a conversion formula and this is given below in its two forms:

$$°C = \tfrac{5}{9} \, (°F - 32)$$
$$°F = (\tfrac{9}{5} \times °C) + 32$$

When using the formula for your calculator, remember to work out the part within the brackets first. Examples will illustrate the method:

1. Convert 64°F.
    First evaluate (64 − 32). Multiply by 5. Divide by 9. The answer is 17·8°C (to one decimal place).

2. Convert 37°C.
    Multiply 37 by 9. Divide by 5. Add 32.
    The answer is 98·6°F.

Some examples to try
9j Convert the following to °C:
   (i) 100°F   (ii) 74°F   (iii) 165°F   (iv) 18°F
9k Convert to °F:
   (i) 40°C   (ii) 85°C   (iii) 7°C   (iv) − 12°C

CONVERSION FACTORS

	From	To	Multiply by
Length			
	Centimetres	Inches	0·3937008
	Inches	Centimetres	2·5399999
	Metres	Feet	3·2808400
	Feet	Metres	0·3047999
	Metres	Yards	1·0936133
	Yards	Metres	0·9143998
	Kilometres	Miles	0·6213710
	Miles	Kilometres	1·6093444
Area			
	Square centimetres	Square inches	0·1550003
	Square inches	Square centimetres	6·4516004
	Square metres	Square feet	10·763909
	Square feet	Square metres	0·0929030
	Square metres	Square yards	1·1959898
	Square yards	Square metres	0·8361273
	Square kilometres	Square miles	0·3861021
	Square miles	Square kilometres	2·589988
Volume			
	Cubic centimetres	Cubic inches	0·0610237
	Cubic inches	Cubic centimetres	16·387070
	Cubic metres	Cubic feet	35·314670
	Cubic feet	Cubic metres	0·0283168
	Cubic yards	Cubic metres	0·7645549
	Cubic metres	Cubic yards	1·3079507

	From	*To*	*Multiply by*
Weight			
	Grammes	Ounces	0·0352739
	Ounces	Grammes	28·349523
	Kilogrammes	Pounds	2·2046224
	Pounds	Kilogrammes	0·4535924
	Tonnes	Tons	0·9842065
	Tons	Tonnes	1·0160469
Liquid capacity			
	Millilitres	Fluid ounces	0·0351960
	Fluid ounces	Millilitres	28·41225
	Litres	Pints	1·7598049
	Pints	Litres	0·5682448
	Litres	Gallons	0·2199756
	Gallons	Litres	4·5459585
Volume/capacity			
	Litres	Cubic inches	61·025472
	Cubic inches	Litres	0·0163866
	Litres	Cubic feet	0·0353156
	Cubic feet	Litres	28·316044

N.B. measures given above are Imperial, where appropriate, and not U.S.

10

MORE FIGURE FUN

Here is a little more light relief concerned with number churning. Most of these examples relate to properties of numbers.

Thirteens
In *Figure Fun* in Chapter 4 some interesting results were found when the numbers 1 to 6 were divided in turn by 7. Other numbers perform in somewhat similar fashion.

Divide 1 by 13 and note the figures.

Divide 2 by 13 and note the figures.

But, you say, this is not similar to the case of the sevens! Just a moment, please!

Divide 3 by 13 and note the figures. Any comment?

And what about 4 by 13?

Now it appears to be working! But what happened with 2 by 13?

Divide 5 by 13 and compare with your earlier results.

You should now be able to spot what is happening. Continue your calculations by dividing 6 by 13, 7 by 13 and so on up to 12 divided by 13.

There are other fractions which, when expressed as decimals, exhibit similar patterns to those seen in the cases of 7 and 13, but these are beyond the capacity of normal calculators to display the results. For example if we take the fractions $\frac{1}{17}$, $\frac{2}{17}$, $\frac{3}{17}$, on to $\frac{16}{17}$ we find that there is a recurring pattern of 16 digits. That is to say when we divide 1 by 17 we obtain a decimal which after the sixteenth figure repeats the first sixteen figures again and so on, just as we found in the case of 7. Moreover this is true for all the other 15 fractions except that the sixteen figures which are repeated are the same for every fraction but arranged in a different order.

Odd or even

Choose any number (a small one initially!) and enter it into your calculator. Now proceed as follows:

If the number is even, divide by 2.

If the number is odd, multiply by 3 and add 1.

Look at the answer you obtain and apply the same rules. Proceed in this manner until you can go no further.

As an example, suppose 37 was chosen originally.

37 is odd, so multiply by 3 and add 1.	Result = 112
This is even, so divide by 2.	Result = 56
This is even, so divide by 2.	Result = 28
This is even, so divide by 2.	Result = 14
This is even, so divide by 2.	Result = 7
This is odd, so multiply by 3 and add 1.	Result = 22
This is even, so divide by 2.	Result = 11
This is odd, so multiply by 3 and add 1.	Result = 34

Continuing in this manner, the sequence of numbers is

17, 52, 26, 13, 40, 20, 10, 5, 16, 8, 4, 2, 1.

Once this point is reached you can go no further. If you regard 1 as odd and try to proceed, you return to 1 in three moves!

But does this occur for all numbers?

We may alter the process by a minor adjustment. The first rule is the same as before, but the second rule is that if the number is odd, you multiply by 3 and *subtract* 1. You are left to discover for yourself what happens in this case. A word of warning: note your answers carefully.

The Natural numbers

The numbers 1, 2, 3, 4, 5, ... are called the natural numbers;
sometimes they are called counting numbers for an obvious
reason. We are going to consider the sums of various com-
binations of natural numbers.

Use your calculator to find the sums of the first, first two,
first three, first four ... natural numbers, setting down your
answers as:

$$
\begin{aligned}
1 &= 1 \\
1 + 2 &= 3 \\
1 + 2 + 3 &= 6 \\
1 + 2 + 3 + 4 &= 10
\end{aligned}
$$

Continue for as long as you wish.

Suppose n is the number of natural numbers which you have
added together on any one line above, substitute that value of
n in the formula $\frac{1}{2}n(n + 1)$. For example, taking the last line
above, there were four terms, so put $n = 4$ and the formula
becomes $\frac{1}{2} \times 4 \times (4 + 1) = 10$. Check the formula for the
sum of the numbers in other cases. (N.B. The formula is a
special case of that for an arithmetic progression given in
Chapter 14.)

Next, sum the squares of the natural numbers by means of
your calculator and again set down your results:

$$
\begin{aligned}
1^2 &= 1 &&= 1 \\
1^2 + 2^2 &= 1 + 4 &&= 5 \\
1^2 + 2^2 + 3^2 &= 1 + 4 + 9 &&= 14 \\
1^2 + 2^2 + 3^3 + 4^2 &= \ldots &&= 30
\end{aligned}
$$

Continue for as long as you wish.

This time the formula to compare is $\frac{1}{6}n(n + 1)(2n + 1)$,
where n is the number of terms and the whole formula gives
you the sum of the squares of the first n natural numbers.
For example, if $n = 4$, the sum will be $\frac{1}{6} \times 4 \times (4 + 1) \times
(8 + 1) = 30$, which is the same result that was obtained above
by summing the individual terms. Check the formula against

some of the other sums of squares which you have obtained by using the long method.

Finally, sum the cubes of the first n natural numbers. As before, do the calculation by summing the individual terms using the calculator and make a note of the results.

$$1^3 = 1$$
$$1^3 + 2^3 = 1 + 8 = 9$$
$$1^3 + 2^3 + 3^3 = 1 + 8 + 27 = 36$$
$$1^3 + 2^3 + 3^3 + 4^3 = 100$$

Again, continue for as long as you wish.

Instead of giving a formula which will enable you to obtain these totals, we are going to look at the problem this time in a different way. Turn back to the first example above where the natural numbers were added and notice the first four results; alongside them write the results above.

Sum of n numbers	Sum of cubes of n numbers
1	1
3	9
6	36
10	100

What do you notice? See if the result holds good for other values beyond the first four natural numbers.

This time instead of quoting a formula we may state the result in words:

The sum of the cubes of the first n natural numbers is equal to the square of the sum of the first n natural numbers. Or if we require this in number form,

$$1^3 + 2^3 + 3^3 + 4^3 + \ldots + n^3 =$$
$$(1 + 2 + 3 + 4 + \ldots + n)^2$$

11

CALCULATIONS AROUND
THE HOUSE

You will have realized from your reading in this book so far
that the calculator need not be used solely in one's job and that
it can play a valuable part in dealing with other everyday
calculations such as household finance. Chapters 6, 7, and 8 in
particular have shown the calculator being used to handle
financial matters which concern every householder. In this
chapter the calculations are concerned specifically with matters
of personal finance.

Household bills
Many people accept a bill which is sent to them as being
correct and pay it as a matter of course. If they checked their
bills more carefully they might be surprised to discover how
often they are incorrect! There are two main points at which
errors occur and both of these should be checked carefully:

1. *Check the quantities* for which you are being charged.
This is most important since the bill just cannot be correct
if it is wrong in this respect.
2. *Check the calculations* on the bill. This means checking the
individual items (e.g. so many at so much) and the overall
addition. If there are any discounts or additions (e.g. V.A.T.)
check these also.

The first of these two points is suspect because it is subject
to human error. We are accustomed to putting our faith in
machines such as calculators and are apt to forget that their

information is fed to them by humans who are liable to make errors. Most of the stories one hears about computers doing funny things are not attributable to the computer at all but to the people who feed information or instructions into it wrongly. When you go to the supermarket your bill is worked out on a printing calculator and you are given the slip with the total at the bottom. The chances that the addition is wrong are very small indeed, so most of pay without question. However, it is alarming how many of these bills are incorrect.

The trouble lies in the listing of the items by the persons at the check-out. Next time you visit the supermarket take care to keep the bill and as you transfer the items from the super-market basket to your shopping bag or car-boot, tick off with a pencil the prices on the list one by one. Alternatively add the price of each article into your calculator as you select it. Lots of people who have done this have been surprised to find that as many as a third of their bills are wrongly itemized. Be warned! This is not a matter for use of your calculator but for use of common sense!

The same warning applies to all bills, of course, and the correct way to check any which are received is to start with the individual items and make sure that quantities and prices are correct. Next use the calculator to work out the price on each individual line (so many at so much each). Finally check the overall addition. If your calculator has a memory the overall addition can be taking place all the time since, as you work out each individual line, the total for that line can be added to the memory. Hence at the end the overall total is immediately available from the memory.

Certain types of household bills have technical points which some people do not fully understand and so pay without question. The more common of these are treated individually below and the technicalities explained. But the principle is still the same and you will notice how the two points above are applied. I have used bills typical in the United Kingdom as examples; again the principles will apply elsewhere.

The importance of what has gone so far in this chapter cannot be over-emphasized. If you follow the advice given, you should find that you have recovered the cost of your calculator within weeks!

Electricity bills

These are common to all households and are too often accepted as being correct without any question. The fact that decimals of a penny appear (like 0·921p) puts off many people, but if you have a calculator it should cause no trouble.

Start at the beginning. When the official comes to read the meter, go and read it yourself and make a note of the reading. If you forgot or it was inconvenient to do so, take the reading when the bill arrives. It will not be the same, but at least it should have read less when he called than it does now! You are checking for human error again.

The bill gives the "present" reading which you have just checked and also the "previous" reading. This "previous" reading should be the "present" reading on your last bill, so get your last bill and check this point.

Next check the tariff, i.e. the scale on which you are charged. This is often given as a code number, e.g. D 13, and a list of codes and their corresponding charges is given on the back of the bill. If this does not appear on the bill ask at your Electricity Board for a leaflet stating the tariff for your area.

Some domestic tariffs for electricity are arranged in two parts, e.g. a certain number of units at one price and the rest at another price. The number of units at each price and the cost per unit in each case will be stated on the bill. Thus it may say that the first 59 units are at 3·950p per unit and the rest are charged at 0·921p per unit. Having established that these rates are correct, proceed to check the calculations. To illustrate the method an imaginary bill is given below.

Meter readings		Units	Tariff	Pence per unit	Amount
Present	Previous				
11677	11056	59	D13	3·950	2·33
		562	D13	0·921	5·18
					————
			Total now due		£7·51

Enter into your calculator the present reading (11677) and subtract the previous reading (11056). Display now reads 621. Subtract the number of units at the first tariff (59) and check that the remainder (562) agrees with the number stated on the bill. Multiply this last number by the appropriate pence per unit (0·921); the result is in pence (517·602) and should be corrected to the nearest penny (518). This agrees with the £5·18 shown. Now re-enter the number of units at the other rate (59) and multiply by the rate (3·950) to obtain the answer 233·05. Correcting to the nearest penny this agrees with the stated 2·33. Finally check the addition.

Gas bills

These are a little more difficult than electricity bills because the consumption of gas is recorded in cubic feet and the charge is made per therm. The idea of cubic feet of gas is simple enough; the meter measures the volume of gas that passes through it into your house. But whereas a unit of electricity will give the same amount of heat or light in any part of the country, what you can get from a cubic foot of gas varies with what one might term the "richness" of the gas. Consequently the Gas Board charges you for the heating value of the gas, or as it calls it, the calorific value. This is measured in therms and the number of cubic feet of gas that make up a therm varies in different parts of the country with the different types of gas.

Once more all this information should be given on your bill. If it isn't and you are uncertain, ask for details from your local Gas Board. Usually there is a statement on your bill "Calorific value 100 cu. ft. = . . . therms". For natural gas the number in the space occupied by the dots is around 1·020. As in the case of electricity you are charged according to a certain tariff which is usually given as a tariff code on the bill and the explanation of the various codes is given on the reverse side of the bill.

Checking the bill involves checking the readings and finding the volume of gas consumed as indicated by the meter. This is very similar to what we did in the case of the electricity bill. The readings from your meter are in hundreds of cubic feet and have to be changed into therms. Enter the number of 100's cu. ft. into your calculator and multiply by the number given as explained in the last paragraph. For example, if you have consumed 137 hundreds of cubic feet of gas and the bill states "Calorific value of 100 cu. ft. = 1·020 therms", you multiply 137 by 1·020 to obtain 139·74. You will be charged on a consumption of 139·74 therms and this is stated on the bill.

Having made the above calculation, the rest consists of checking the charge according to the tariff code. Some gas tariffs work as the example given above for electricity with the first batch of therms at a high charge and the rest at a lower rate. In such cases check as you did with the electricity bill above. Other tariffs include a standing charge per quarter with the number of therms used being charged at a flat rate. Such tariffs are checked by multiplying the number of therms consumed by the rate per therm and then adding the fixed charge.

One feature of gas sales is that different tariffs are offered and usually the choice has to be made by the customer. This

can be a little bewildering although explanatory leaflets should
be available. The calculations involved are described below.

Everything depends on how much gas you use and how you
use it, so the first things you need are your bills which cover
a typical year. Note the number of therms consumed per
quarter; is it fairly constant or does it fluctuate considerably?
For example if you use gas only for heating purposes, you are
going to have a heavy consumption in winter and a very light
one in summer. When people are considering choice of tariff,
the annual consumption is usually taken as a basis for decision,
but if consumption does vary widely it is as well to do calculations on a quarterly basis. Many tariffs involve a fixed standing
charge per quarter, in consequence of which the charges per
therm are reduced. When considering the true cost of the gas
we should spread the standing charge over the total therms
consumed. An example will illustrate.

Suppose the choice of tariffs is as follows:

General credit tariff
    Fixed standing charge   £1·00 per quarter
    Gas consumption charge   15·00p per therm

Gold Star tariff
    Fixed standing charge   £3·00 per quarter
    Gas consumption charge   9·50p per therm

Imagine that your total consumption for the year was 705
therms and do an overall calculation in each case:

General credit tariff

Standing charge per year	$4 \times 1·00$	$=$	£4·00
Consumption charge	$705 \times 15·00p$	$=$	£105·75
	Total	$=$	£109·75

Gold Star tariff

Standing charge per year	$4 \times 3·00$	$=$	£12·00
Consumption charge	$705 \times 9·50p$	$=$	£66·97
	Total	$=$	£78·97

Clearly the Gold Star tariff is the better choice in these circumstances. What are the actual costs per therm? For the Gold Star tariff it is $\frac{78 \cdot 97}{705}$ = £0·1120 per therm (or 11·20p) and for the General credit tariff it is 15·57p per therm. But notice that this is an average price over the year. In a quarter where you use little gas the price per therm will rise, but will be compensated by a fall in the price per therm in a quarter when you use a large amount. This variation does not matter under normal circumstances and when you are considering tariffs which are of similar construction, but if we are comparing a tariff with a standing charge with one without, it can be important. In such cases it is as well to do calculations for each quarter, since the pattern of consumption can make a difference. To take an extreme example, if, in one quarter, you only used one therm of gas and were on the General credit tariff above, then that therm of gas would cost you £1·15. The only way to find the best tariff to choose in cases such as this is to take your bills for a typical year and use your calculator to find from actual consumption what the costs would be using different tariffs.

Before leaving the calculation of gas bills we might return to the two tariffs above and ask what is the change-over point where it becomes cheaper to use one tariff rather than the other. The calculation is simple: first find the difference in price of the standing charge, then the difference in the cost per therm.

In the above example:

difference in standing charge = £2·00 per quarter

difference in cost per therm = 5·50p per therm.

You have the option of paying an extra £2 per quarter or an extra 5·50p per therm so divide the difference in standing charge (expressed in pence) by the difference in cost per therm, i.e. $\dfrac{200}{5\cdot50} = 36\cdot36$. This represents the number of therms that could be bought with the increased standing charge and if we multiply this by four to make it cover the year, it means that if you consume less than 145 therms per year it is cheaper to use the General credit tariff; above this quantity the Gold Star tariff is cheaper.

Taxation(1): Income Tax

This is a form of direct taxation, i.e. it is charged directly on your income and not indirectly on, for example, items which you buy. Income tax in Britain is now charged at a certain percentage of your taxable income, the percentage varying with the amount of income.

Your taxable income is your actual income less certain allowances for expenses involved in your work, insurance payments, family commitments, etc. This is not the place to explain the various allowances and how to claim them; in any case these are liable to change from year to year. A guide to income tax would help you here. But note that some expenses are allowed in full, whereas others are allowed in part only. You should keep a record of allowances which apply in your case so that you can calculate your total allowance and this must be deducted from your total income before you make any further calculations. Note that total income includes income from your employment or business, dividends, royalties, etc.

Once you have calculated your expenses, you need to calculate your personal allowance according to current rates. This depends upon your family commitments. Thus a single person may get an allowance of £595, a married man £775, each child under the age of 16 an allowance of £235 and so on. Again these allowances vary from time to time, so you need to obtain the up-to-date figures. Total all these allowances and deduct from your total income. You pay tax on what is left.

The rate of tax is differential. As an example, the tax rate in a recent year was 30 per cent for the first £5000, 40 per cent for the next £1000, 45 per cent for the next £1000 and so on. Again you should find the current rates. The calculation of the amount of tax to be paid should not prove difficult using your calculator. If you pay tax under PAYE, where the tax is deducted by monthly or weekly instalments from what you earn as it is paid, you should divide by 12 or 52 as the case may be.

A typical example is given:

	£
Income for year	4800
Allowed expenses	160
	4640
Allowance (married with one child)	1010
	3630
Tax paid on	3630

Annual tax = 30 per cent of £3630
    = £1089
Monthly tax = £90·75

Taxation (2): *Rates*
This system of local taxation is unique to the United Kingdom. The basic idea in the calculation of local government rates is that they are based on a certain monetary value attached to your house and for every £1 of that value you are required to pay a certain sum.

Each property is given a value which is related to the amount which may be expected to be obtained if the property was let at an annual rental. The total amount of these rateable values, as they are called, for the local authority area is the amount on which the local authority makes its annual charge. It makes an estimate each year of the money it needs to provide essential services, e.g. education, police, refuse disposal, etc., and then averages this out over the total rateable value. To take a simple example, if the total rateable value for an authority's area was 10 million pounds and it estimated that it was going to spend 6 million pounds in the coming year, it would have to charge a rate which was six-tenths of the rateable value of each property; in other words it would charge 60p for each £1 of rateable value. So if your house had a rateable value of £120 you would have to pay 120 × 60p (i.e. £72) for your annual rate.

Certain adjustments are made in the levying of the rate. For example, industrial properties may be required to pay a different rate from household properties. Also the Government makes certain grants to local authorities to assist them financially. But as far as you are concerned, when your rate bill arrives three items should be stated on it:

1. The rateable value of your property.
2. The rate to be levied, expressed as so much in the £1.
3. The actual rates which you have to pay.

From what has been said, it should be clear that item 3 will be the product of items 1 and 2.

Example: Rateable value = £255

General rate in the £1 = £0·432

Rates payable = 255 × 0·432 = £110·16

Sometimes other charges are also based on the rateable value, e.g. water charges, but these are calculated in exactly the same way.

Example: Rateable value as above, water charge = £0·055 in the £1

Water rate payable = 255 × 0·055 = £14·025

Shopping

One of the great difficulties of shopping these days is that most goods on sale are pre-packaged and packages are not standard-ized. There were the days when if you bought a pot of jam at the stores you knew it contained 1 lb. of jam without having to read the label, but this is no longer the case! Some still contain 1 lb. but others contain less although they are often sold in jars contrived to make them look as if they contain more than they do! And jam is but one example. Fortunately many countries have a requirement by law that the contents of a package shall be stated on the package itself.

But even so, there are some peculiar sizes of contents – $10\frac{1}{2}$ ounces, $1\frac{3}{4}$ pounds, $1 \cdot 2$ pints and the like. And an increas-ing amount of material is being packaged in metric measures. How does the housewife compare prices under these circum-stances? The calculator can be invaluable in this situation. Admitted it would be time-consuming to compare prices of every single article purchased at the stores, but for the more costly items it is well worthwhile to compare the prices of different brands and the process need take only a few seconds with the calculator.

There is no need to do complicated calculations to find out how much you will save, since you are only interested in the best buy. Possibly the quickest way is to find the cost of a unit measure in each case. Take for example two bottles of liquid, the first of which is stated to contain $35 \cdot 2$ fluid ounces and sells for 62 pence, while the second contains 2 pints (40 fluid ounces) and costs 69 pence. The easy way here is to find the cost of a fluid ounce in each case and to do this we must divide the cost by the number of fluid ounces. The first gives a price of $1 \cdot 76$ pence per fluid ounce (do not worry about the further decimal places) and the second gives $1 \cdot 725$ pence. The second is the better buy, provided the liquid is equally good for its purpose.

If you are anxious to know how much you save and want to compare the prices rather than just decide which is the cheaper, the method to adopt is to find how much it would cost to buy the *same* quantity, for example 2 pints in the example quoted. To do this, find the cost per fluid ounce for the first bottle in same way as above, then multiply by 40 to find the cost of 40 fluid ounces. So we would divide 35·2 into 62 and multiply the result by 40. The answer is 70·45 pence. So purchasing the second bottle will save you roughly $1\frac{1}{2}$ pence for two pints.

Here is one further example to illustrate the two methods. A 14 ounce package costs 39 pence and a $12\frac{1}{2}$ ounce package of the same type of goods costs 33 pence; which is the better buy? Method 1:

14 ounce package costs $\dfrac{39}{14} = 2\cdot786\text{p}$ per ounce.

$12\frac{1}{2}$ ounce package costs $\dfrac{33}{12\cdot5} = 2\cdot64\text{p}$ per ounce.

Method 2:
14 ounce package of the first costs 39 pence

A 14 ounce package of the second would cost $\dfrac{33}{12\cdot5} \times 14$

$$= 36\cdot96 \text{ pence.}$$

The examples given above are in Imperial units (although notice that the 35·2 fluid ounces of the first example is one litre). If measures are given in metric units, the method of dealing with the problem is exactly the same. The only difficulty arises when one package is in Imperial measure and the other is in metric. Fortunately some manufacturers who package their products in metric measure also state on the label the equivalent Imperial measure. In the case of this not being so, a little more calculation is involved and you should refer back to Chapter 9 for details of metric conversions.

Home decorating

The calculator can be particularly useful when estimating
the quantities of materials required in home decorating. The
simplest type of calculation required is that of area. If you
are painting the walls or ceiling this type of calculation will
guide you as to the amount of paint to buy. Suppose you have
a room measuring 12 feet by $10\frac{1}{2}$ feet. The area of the ceiling
is easy to calculate: $12 \times 10\frac{1}{2} = 126$ square feet.

If the height of the room is $8\frac{1}{2}$ feet, to find the wall area
you simply multiply this by the total distance around the
room, i.e. $8\cdot5 \times 2 \times (12 + 10\frac{1}{2}) = 382\cdot5$ square feet. Notice
that we can ignore doors and windows. Painting around these
always takes some paint and in any case it is advisable to have
some paint left over. Most tins of paint tell you the area which
you can expect to cover with a given amount of paint; if it is
not on the tin the shop assistant will advise. Different types of
paint spread at different rates, so no rule can be given which
covers all cases. If you have any irregular shaped areas, refer
to the next chapter of this book.

When you intend to paper the walls or ceiling with wallpaper
it is not sufficient to find the area and divide this by the area
of a roll (or piece as it is usually called) of wallpaper. Remember that you are going to have wastage for pattern matching
and in some places (for example, by the side of a door) you
may only be using a narrow strip from a length seven or eight
feet long; the remaining piece may not fit anywhere else and
will thus be wasted.

Decorators' suppliers usually have reference tables which
state the number of pieces required for rooms of varying sizes,
but you can make your own estimate. Present-day wallpapers
are 51 cm. wide, so you need to measure the length and breadth
of the room in metres and divide the distance round by $0\cdot51$
to find the number of strips which you are going to need. For

a room with normal door and window space you should ignore these.

The standard length of a piece of wallpaper is 10 metres so you next need to find how many strips of the required length you are going to be able to cut from one piece by dividing 10 by the height of your room in metres. Ignore any fractions since you will have some wastage for pattern matching. Having found the number of strips you will get out of one piece, divide this into your calculation of the total number of strips you require, to obtain the estimate of the total number of pieces which you should purchase.

Example:

Room – 3·6 metres by 3·2 metres and 2·4 metres high.

Distance around room = $2 \times (3·6 + 3·2) = 13·6$ metres.

Number of strips required 0·51 metres wide $= \dfrac{13·6}{0·51} =$ 26·6 or 27 whole strips.

Length of one piece = 10 metres

Number of strips per piece $= \dfrac{10}{2·4} = 4·16$

or 4 whole strips.

Hence number of pieces needed $= \dfrac{27}{4} = 6·75$.

You purchase 7 pieces of wallpaper.

12

AREA AND VOLUME

Most measurements are made by the use of an instrument: a ruler or tape to measure a length, a measuring jug to measure capacity, scales to measure weight, a protractor to measure angles and so on. To find the required measure we simply apply the instrument and take a reading; this gives the result in the appropriate units.

But there are two measurements in particular which involve calculation before a result is obtained. These are area and volume. This is because the units in which we express area and volume are derived from measurements of length. Thus a square metre is the amount of area in a square measuring one metre by one metre. Notice that this area does not have to be square or any particular shape, provided that it is equal to the amount of area we have just stated. But the point is that before we can calculate the area, we have to measure some length. The same is true of volume: a cubic metre is the amount of space within a cube measuring one metre along each side. Again it does not have to be that shape but it must occupy the equivalent amount of space.

This chapter is concerned with the various calculations which are required to find areas and volumes of objects of different shapes.

Area
The simplest area to find is that of a rectangle. If this is 4 metres long and 3 metres wide, we can imagine it to be

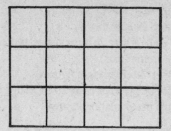

Fig. 1

divided up into squares measuring one metre by one metre and there will be 12 such squares as in Fig. 1. Thus the area must be 12 square metres. This result can be obtained simply by multiplying the number of metres in the length (4) by the number of metres in the width (3). What we are doing is multiplying the number of metre squares in a row by the number of rows.

This is the basis for all rectangular area calculations: area = length × width. Thus a rectangular lawn measuring 5·4 metres by 6·8 metres has an area of 36·72 square metres. The area of the lawn may be very important when buying and applying fertilizer, for example.

A shape such as a rectangle on a flat surface is called a plane figure and areas of various types of plane figure are calculated by the use of appropriate formulae. Some of these are given below without proof and their use will be demonstrated. If proofs are required the reader is referred to elementary mathematical textbooks.

Plane figure	*Area formula*
Rectangle	length × width
Parallelogram	length of base × perpendicular height
Triangle	$\frac{1}{2}$ base length × perpendicular height
Trapezium	$\frac{1}{2}$ (sum of parallel sides × distance between them)

Plane figure   *Area formula*
Circle πr^2 (where r = radius)
Ellipse πab (where 2a is the major and 2b the
                      minor axis)

The value of $\pi = 3 \cdot 1415927$ (to eight figures).

An example will now be given of each of the above figures and the use of the formula in calculating its area.

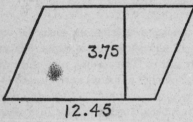

12.45   **Fig. 2**

(1) Parallelogram. Fig. 2.

Taking one side as base, the height must be measured perpendicularly to this. In the diagram, base = 12·45 m. and height = 3·75 m. Hence area is 46·6875 square metres.

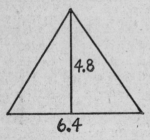

6.4   **Fig. 3**

(2) Triangle. Fig. 3.

In the diagram the base is given as 6·4 cm. and the height is 4·8 cm.

Area = $\frac{1}{2} \times$ base $\times$ height
     = $0\cdot5 \times 6\cdot4 \times 4\cdot8$
     = $15\cdot36$ sq. cm.

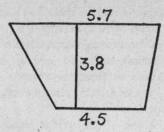

Fig. 4

(3) Trapezium. Fig. 4.

Measure the length of the two parallel sides and the perpendicular distance between them. Here the parallel sides are 5·7 and 4·5 cm. and the distance between them is 3·8 cm.

Area $= 0·5 \times (5·7 + 4·5) \times 3·8$

$= 19·38$ sq. cm.

(4) Circle.

If the length of the diameter of a circle is divided into the length of its circumference, we obtain a ratio which is constant whatever the size of the circle. This constant, however, does not have an exact value, so we denote it by π (the Greek letter "pi"). The value of this constant is given in the table above to eight figures which will be adequate for most purposes. From our definition it will be seen that if we wish to obtain the length of the circumference of a circle, we find the length of the diameter and multiply by π. Suppose we have a circle whose diameter is 30 cm., then the length of the circumference will be $30 \times 3·1415927$ cm. or $94·247781$ cm. This is a remarkable degree of accuracy and will only be true if the measurement of 30 cm. for the diameter is *exact*. A more reasonable answer to give in this case would be $94·2$ cm. or even just 94 cm. This matter of the accuracy of measurement and the accuracy of the answer as written down is dealt with more fully in Chapter 13. Suffice to say now that an answer involving six decimal places would be out of order for this particular problem. Accepting this, it is rather pointless always to use a value of π

expressed to eight figures. Notice that if we used 3·14 as the value the answer would be 94·2. So although a value of π to eight places is given (because eight-figure display is the most common for calculators), we would need to use this value only when a high degree of accuracy was needed.

The value 3·142 is useful, easily remembered, and the one most generally adopted.

Next suppose the area of the circle is required. Here we use the formula πr^2, where r is the length of the radius. In the example above, r will be 15, so the area is 3·142 × 15 × 15 = 706·95 sq. cm. 706·86 is the answer if the full value of π is used and the result corrected to two decimal places; the difference is negligible.

(5) Ellipse.

The longest distance measured across an ellipse is called its major axis and the shortest distance across is known as the minor axis. The area of an ellipse is obtained by multiplying half of each length together and multiplying the result by π. So an ellipse with major axis 14·5 cm. and minor axis 8·2 cm. would have an area of 93·40 sq. cm.

There are certain solids whose surface area may be required. This particularly applies to cylinders and spheres and formulae are given below for these. In the case of the surface area of rectangular boxes, these are easily found by calculating the area of each of the faces and adding them.

Curved surface area of a cylinder = $2\pi rh$

(This is the area of the cylinder without the ends: r is the radius of the base and h is the height of the cylinder.)

Area of the surface of a sphere is $4\pi r^2$, where r is the radius of the sphere.

The curved surface area of a cylinder of radius 40 cm. and height 150 cm. will be 2 × π × 40 × 150 = 37704 sq. cm. If the cylinder had been closed (i.e. with two ends on it), the *total* surface area would be calculated by finding the curved surface area as above and adding the area of the two ends (use the memory to hold the first answer if your calculator has this facility). One end has area $3 \cdot 142 \times 40 \times 40 = 5027$ sq. cm., so the total area would be 47758 sq. cm.

The area of the surface of a sphere of radius 12 cm. is $4 \times 3 \cdot 142 \times 12 \times 12 = 1810$ sq. cm.

There are corresponding formulae for other areas and these can be found in mathematical textbooks. Substitution and calculation follow the lines of the various examples given above.

Volume

The calculation of volume also depends upon the use of various formulae and these will not be proved here. The simplest example is the rectangular block (e.g. a brick) where the volume is obtained by multiplying together length, width and height. Notice however that when the length and the width are multiplied together, the area of the base is obtained. So another way in which this volume could be found would be to multiply the area of the base by the height. The principle is capable of extension and of use when finding the volume of many solids whose sides are perpendicular to the base, e.g. a cylinder. In the case of a cylinder the area of the base, is the area of a circle, which is πr^2, and the volume is obtained by multiplying this by the height, h. This corresponds with the formula below, but is a useful way of remembering it.

Solid	*Volume*
Rectangular block	length $\times$ width $\times$ height
Cylinder	$\pi r^2 h$
Cone	$\frac{1}{3} \pi r^2 h$
Sphere	$\frac{4}{3} \pi r^3$

The following are examples on finding volumes of various solids.

(1) Rectangular block.

A trench of rectangular section measures 2·5 metres wide, 1·5 metres deep and 30 metres long; what volume of earth has been removed?

The volume = 2·5 × 1·5 × 30 = 112·5 cubic metres.

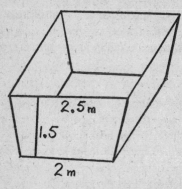

Fig. 5

(2) A trench with sloping sides. Fig. 5.

Imagine the same problem as above but with the sides of the trench sloping inwards so that the width at the foot of the trench is only 2 metres. The section is in the shape of a trapezium as shown in the diagram. Since the sides are perpendicular to this trapezium, we find the volume by calculating the area of the trapezium and multiplying by the total length.

Area of trapezium = ½ (2·5 + 2) × 1·5 = 3·375 sq. m.

Hence volume = 3·375 × 30 = 101·25 cubic metres.

In using the calculator the whole calculation can be done as one continuous process.

(3) Find the volume of a cylindrical tank of height 2·2 metres and base radius 0·7 metres.

Volume = π × 0·7 × 0·7 × 2·2 = 3·387 cubic metres.

(4) The volume of a cone of height 2·2 metres and base radius 0·7 metres will be one-third that of the cylinder in example (3). Hence its volume is 1·129 cubic metres.

(5) The volume of a sphere of radius 18 cm. is $\frac{4}{3} \times 3 \cdot 142 \times 18 \times 18 \times 18$. Notice that the constant facility on the calculator could be used to evaluate 18^3. The volume is 24432 cubic cm.

So far we have been dealing with solids and plane figures of regular shape. The problem of finding areas and volumes of irregular shapes is much more complex and calls for a variety of methods, many of them involving higher mathematics. We shall deal with certain simple cases here. The most simple are those of composite areas or composite bodies. These are plane shapes or solids which can easily be sub-divided into some of the regular shapes above mentioned. Thus we may have a shape something like that surrounded by a running track which would be made up of a rectangle with a semi-circle at each of its ends. Finding the area consists of finding the area of the constituent parts and adding them. Another example is to find the area of a quadrilateral shape; the best method is to divide the figure into two triangles by drawing a diagonal and then find the area of each triangle.

By irregular shapes, however, we usually mean those shapes which have no simple outlines made up of straight lines, circles, etc. These areas and volumes are calculated by approximation methods and the electronic calculator can prove particularly useful with the fair amount of working needed.

Area: Trapezoidal rule

The Trapezoidal rule is a method of finding the area of irregular shapes and is best explained by examples. The first example will establish the rule.

Example 1: We wish to find the area shown in fig. 6 which consists of the space between two parallel lines (AO and BC), a straight line (OC) and a curve forming the other boundary (AB).

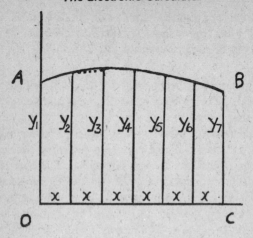

Fig. 6

Divide the area into a number of strips as shown and suppose the width of each of these is x units. Let the heights of the lines dividing the strips be y_1, y_2, y_3, ... y_7 as shown. Next join up the points where the perpendiculars cut the curve by a series of straight lines. (See broken line to show this in area y_3). Once these straight lines have been drawn we have a number (here six) of trapezia whose area together is almost that of the original area bounded by the curve. But the area of a trapezium is given above as $\frac{1}{2}$ (sum of parallel sides) × (distance between them).

So the area of the first strip is $\frac{1}{2}(y_1 + y_2) \times x$

area of second strip is $\frac{1}{2}(y_2 + y_3) \times x$

and so on.

By adding the above, the total area $= (\frac{1}{2}y_1 + y_2 + y_3 + y_4 + y_5 + y_6 + \frac{1}{2}y_7) \times x$

Thus if the strips are 0·5 cm. wide and the heights are as follows:

$$y_1 = 4 \cdot 7 \text{ cm.}$$
$$y_2 = 5 \cdot 3 \text{ cm.}$$
$$y_3 = 5 \cdot 5 \text{ cm.}$$
$$y_4 = 5 \cdot 6 \text{ cm.}$$
$$y_5 = 5 \cdot 7 \text{ cm.}$$
$$y_6 = 5 \cdot 5 \text{ cm.}$$
$$y_7 = 5 \cdot 4 \text{ cm.}$$

then the total area will be approximately

$$(2 \cdot 35 + 5 \cdot 3 + 5 \cdot 5 + 5 \cdot 6 + 5 \cdot 7 + 5 \cdot 5 + 2 \cdot 7) \times 0 \cdot 5$$

which is 16·325 sq. cm.

With the trapezoidal rule, the greater the number of strips taken, the more accurate the result will be. However, more strips means more measurement, so one has to strike a balance. The method may be applied to a much more irregular shape such as the one below. In this case it will be noted that the base line with the "x" measurement runs from one point on the boundary to another so that the first and last values of y will be zero. The length of y is also measured *across* the base line, to include both sides.

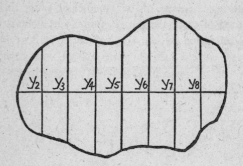

Fig. 7

Example 2: Fig. 7.

The measurements are for an area of land and the value of x is 10 metres. y_2 to y_8 are respectively 32, 38, 41, 37, 38, 40, 26.

Hence approximate area = (32 + 38 + 41 + 37 + 38 + 40 + 26) × 10 = 2520 square metres.

(N.B. $\frac{1}{2}y_1$ and $\frac{1}{2}y_9$ both equal 0 as the value of y on the extremities is zero).

There are other methods of finding areas by approximation, some of which give more accurate results than the Trapezoidal Rule. An example is Simpson's Rule, but for this and others the reader is referred to a textbook of mathematics. The principle applied above in the Trapezoidal Rule underlies most numberical approximations of this type, both for areas and volumes.

Volumes by approximation

The principle applied to the determination of the volume of a solid is to divide it into a series of cylindrical shapes. These correspond to the trapezia in the plane area above. A typical example would be finding the volume of a barrel. If this is imagined to be divided by a number of cuts parallel to the base at a constant height between each cut, one obtains a series of cylindrical shapes all of the same height. If the mean diameter of each of these shapes was found, the volume of each could be calculated and the total volume of the barrel be determined.

Examples to try

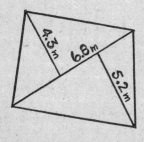

Fig. 8

12a Find the area of the quadrilateral shown in Fig. 8.

12b Find the surface area of a rectangular box measuring 2·6 m. by 1·8 m. by 2·2 m. and the cost of covering this with material costing £5·85 per square metre.

12c If fig. 8 in 12a above represents a lawn and a 7 lb. pack of fertilizer treats 50 square metres, what amount should be used on this lawn?

12d In fig. 7 of Example 2 above, calculate the area from the following information: $x = 2$ metres and y_2 to y_8 are respectively 2·1, 2·5, 3·2, 3·1, 3·0, 3·2, 1·8.

13

APPROXIMATION AND ACCURACY

This chapter is not concerned with operations in the calculator, but with the material which one feeds in and the results received. A calculator has to be used with thoughtfulness and it is the purpose of this book to try to bring an understanding of what is involved in working out certain problems which are being solved on the calculator. It is equally important that we should think carefully about the numbers being used. For example, if you have an eight-digit display calculator and an ordinary ruler, is there much point in saying that the answer to a particular problem based on measurement made with the ruler is 7·5382672 cm?

Much of our calculation depends upon measurement and measurement is not so accurate as we often believe. The scientist and the engineer have means of measuring very precisely, but for others the degree of accuracy is not great. In the example just quoted we would do well if we could measure a line *exactly* to 7·5 cm., i.e. to a millimetre.

Rounding up numbers

When adjusting numbers we have to remember to round up where appropriate. This was dealt with fully in Chapter 3, so it is necessary only to re-state the results. When rounding off a decimal number at a particular place, if the figures following that place are over the half-way mark we increase the number occupying the place by one; otherwise we ignore it. So with 7·5382672, expressing it to one decimal place would be 7·5, since the next figure is a three which is less than the half-way mark; expressing it to two decimal places would be 7·54, since the next figure (8) is over the half-way mark between 7·53 and 7·54.

If you need further help on this you should refer back to the appropriate part of Chapter 3.

Accuracy of data

You are asked to find the area of a rectangle measuring 7·3 metres by 4·8 metres. To find this the length is multiplied by the breadth to give an answer of 35·04 square metres. Is this answer reasonable?

You wish to find the circumference of a circle whose diameter is 3·6 metres. To work this out you multiply the diameter by π (using the value 3·1416) and obtain an answer of 11·309760. Is this a reasonable answer?

Take the second example first. Is 3·6 metres the *exact* diameter? If we brought in the engineer or the scientist to measure it, would he state that it was exactly 3·6 metres? In other words can we write it as 3·60000 . . . adding as many zeros as we wish? The person asking the question probably did the measuring by some means giving tenths of a metre, so he is using that degree of accuracy. What he is saying is that it is not 3·5 metres nor 3·7 metres. But it may be a shade more or less than 3·6, perhaps a hundredth or a thousandth of a metre. So we are dealing with a measurement to an accuracy of one decimal place. We then multiply by a constant and give as our answer another length, i.e. the circumference. Since this depends on the first measurement it cannot be more accurate than our original accuracy, i.e. one decimal place. So whatever the calculator says, we may only give the answer as 11·3 metres.

In the first example, the measurements were to one decimal place, so should the answer be to one decimal place only?

To explain this situation it will be helpful to avoid the use of decimals. 7·3 metres is 7 metres and 3 decimetres or it may be written as 73 decimetres. (There are ten decimetres in a metre). Similarly 4·8 metres is 48 decimetres. So if we multiply these lengths to obtain the area, the answer is 3504 square decimetres. Since the original measurements were accurate to decimetres we may give the answer in square decimetres, which is exactly what we are doing when we state that the answer is 35·04 square metres.

The point of all this is that we must remember to take care when giving answers, since the answer given depends very much on the data on which the calculation is based. It must also depend on common-sense. Division of quantities presents another aspect. Use your calculator to find the length of one part when something 30 cm. long is divided into seven equal parts. Do you state that each part should be cut to a length of 4·2857142 cm? Yet this will be the answer in an eight-digit display calculator.

There are cases where it may be permissible to give an answer with a larger number of decimal places than the initial data; this is when we know the initial data is *exact*. An example is money. An amount such as £3·27 is exact and may be written with as many zeros after it as you wish, i.e. £3·270000 . . .

Suppose we wish to find the simple interest on £3·27 for one year at 1¾ per cent per annum. Substitute in the formula

$$I = \frac{PRT}{100}$$

$$\text{Interest} = \frac{3\cdot27 \times 1\cdot75 \times 1}{100}$$

$$= 0\cdot0572250$$

So the interest would be 5·7225 pence. This is an exact answer and in the circumstances is quite correct. How you would pay it is another matter! However, since this interest is payable yearly, the decimal parts of a penny can make a difference over a number of years.

To sum up, where we know that data is exact, we may give answers to any number of decimal places we wish, but when data is only accurate to a certain number of decimal places answers should be given to the number of decimal places which is warranted by the data. In cases of doubt it is appropriate to give answers only to the same number of decimal places as are found in the data.

Approximation

Much of what has been said so far regarding rounding of numbers has applied to decimals. This chapter started with an example containing the number 7·5382672. This figure was then expressed to one decimal place (as 7·5) and later to two decimal places (7·54). But the same principle of rounding applies to all numbers whether we are dealing with the decimal part or the integral (i.e. whole number) part.

Suppose the example had been 753·82672. To the nearest whole number this would have been 754, since 753·8 is above the "half-way" mark between 753 and 754. If the number was required to the nearest ten, the answer would be 750 because 753 is nearer to this value than it is to 760. Finally if the answer was required to the nearest hundred it would be 800.

It is not often that we are called upon to give numbers so "roughly" as to the nearest hundred, but there are times when the ability to express numbers to nearest tens, hundreds, or even thousands, has its uses. Suppose we are multiplying 462·8 by 34·3; the first number to the nearest hundred is 500 and the second number to the nearest ten is 30, so very roughly we are multiplying 500 by 30. A calculator is hardly required to find the answer to this: 15000. So before doing the actual calculation of the problem, a moment's thought will reveal that the answer is going to be around 15000. If the problem is worked out on the calculator and the answer appears as 847·62, there is an obvious error somewhere; possibly a wrong key has been pressed. Find the correct answer on your calculator and see how close was our rough answer.

This is a very important use of approximate values of numbers. We can rely too much on the calculator! It is rapid and accurate, but it is easy to touch the wrong key or to misread a number, e.g. 758 instead of 785. Entries should always be checked in the display, but this is often overlooked in the anxiety to read and enter the next number. At all times there- fore we should think about what we are doing and have a rough idea of the sort of answer to expect; this applies to calculations done by whatever means are employed – calculator, pen and paper, etc.

Of course, rough checks do not tell us that an answer *is* correct; they indicate whether or not it is a "reasonable" answer. The answer to the example above was 15874·04, but we may make a mistake in copying the answer from the cal- culator and write it as 15784·04. As far as our rough check is concerned we would still accept this as "probably correct".

It is possible to get closer approximations which give a better indication of the truth of an answer. In the example above, we might have taken 460 and 30 as starting numbers; multiplied these give us 13800. This seems further away from the true answer, so would it not have been better to take 460 and 35? Is there any point? It is not easy to multiply 460 by 35 without the calculator; in fact it is not much harder to work out the original problem! Once again we have to use common-sense.

Approximation has other uses. An important use is to be found in Chapter 15 which deals with a method of solving a problem by starting with an approximation to the answer and using certain methods to obtain a closer approximation. Once this has been done, the process may be repeated so that this second approximation may be used to obtain a third (and closer) approximation. And so on until the desired degree of accuracy has been reached.

The method of finding a first approximation in such a case varies with the problem; sometimes there is a very good indication of a likely solution but at other times it is almost a matter of guesswork! Suppose we wished to find the solution of an equation such as $2x^2 - 7x + 4 = 0$ and needed to find an approximate value of x first. What is being sought is a value for x which when substituted for x on the left-hand side of the equation will make it equal to zero.

Looking at the numbers (i.e. coefficients) alone, $2 - 7 + 4$ comes to $- 1$. This is not far from zero, so if we gave x the value of 1 we should be somewhere near a correct answer. However if we wished to find an even better approximation we might try putting another value for x. Put $x = 2$ and the left-hand side becomes $8 - 14 + 4$, which is -2 and seems to indicate that we are moving further from a solution.

Try a value less than $x = 1$; say $0 \cdot 5$. The left-hand side now equals $2 \times (0 \cdot 25) - 7 \times 0 \cdot 5 + 4 = 0 \cdot 5 - 3 \cdot 5 + 4 = 1$. So when $x = 1$, the left-hand side has a value of $- 1$, and when $x = 0 \cdot 5$ it has a value of $+ 1$. Since the required value of 0 lies between these two, a solution for x will be found between $x = 1$ and $x = 0 \cdot 5$; choose $0 \cdot 75$ as a close approximation.

In another example we may wish to find approximately the square root of 92. This is another way of saying that we require a number which when multiplied by itself (i.e. squared) gives 92. Squares are easily worked out and we find that $9^2 = 81$ and $10^2 = 100$. So the number we are looking for must lie between 9 and 10 and $9 \cdot 5$ may be chosen as an approximation to the true answer.

Some examples to try:

13a Find approximate answers to the following problems, then do the full working on your calculator:

$23 \cdot 7 \times 86 \cdot 5 \div 19 \cdot 1$ $(18 \cdot 9 + 31 \cdot 6) \times 63 \cdot 4$

$(37)^2$ $9 \times 8 \times 7 \times 6 \times 5$

13b A cubical box has a side of $6 \cdot 4$ cm. Find its volume, remembering permissible degree of accuracy.

14

SEQUENCES AND SERIES

Enter a number in your calculator, say 7. Now add another number and note the answer. Add this same number again and note the answer. Repeat as often as desired. Suppose the number which you had chosen to add repeatedly was 4, then the answers would give a sequence of numbers as follows:

7, 11, 15, 19, 23, 27, 31, 35, 39, 43, . . .

If your calculator has a constant key which operates on addition, the easy way to do the above problem is to enter 4 as the constant first, then enter 7 in the display and press the + key repeatedly.

Now take the same two numbers and repeat the exercise but this time multiply by the second number instead of adding it. Once more, use the constant key if your machine has this feature. This time the sequence of numbers will be (in our case):

7, 28, 112, 448, 1792, 7168, 28672, 114688, . . .

It is possible to do similar exercises where the operation used is subtraction or division. In each case the electronic calculator enables one to generate the successive terms with a minimum of effort. The type of series which you have been producing is a progression.

Arithmetic progressions

An arithmetic series is one where we are adding or subtracting the same number to each successive term. The first example above is an arithmetic progression (commonly called an "A.P."). The commonest example of an A.P. is ordinary counting. If we count 1, 2, 3, 4, 5, 6, etc. we are saying the terms of an A.P. Of course there are other ways in which we may count, but these are still arithmetic progressions:

(a) Count in twos: 2, 4, 6, 8, 10, . . .

(b) Count in threes starting at 1: 1, 4, 7, 10, 13, . . .

(c) Count in fours starting at 7: (we have seen this before!)

(d) Count backwards in twos from 6: 6, 4, 2, 0, −2, −4, −6, . . .

Look again at (a). Would 1, 3, 5, 7, 9, . . . be a satisfactory answer? And what about 102, 104, 106, 108, 110, . . . ? How does (a) differ from (b), (c) and (d)? There can be no doubt of what is required in any of the last three cases; anyone given the same instructions would produce the same answer. So to be able to generate the terms of an A.P. we need to know the number with which to start (called "the first term") and the number to be added repeatedly (called "the common difference"). In (b), for example, the first term is 1 and the common difference is 3. Notice that for convenience we say "added" but the common difference could be a negative number, in which case the *numerical* difference would be subtracted from successive terms. To illustrate the point, look again at (d) above. The first term is 6 and 2 is being subtracted each time. It could be described alternatively as having a first term of 6 and a common difference of −2 which is added on to each term.

With a calculator it is just as easy to deal with a decimal number as a whole number, so we can easily generate some rather complex A.P.s. For example, the first term may be 3·5 and the common difference 1·2, so that we get the series:

3·5, 4·7, 5·9, 7·1, 8·3, 9·5, . . .

Sometimes a series may be given without either the first term or the common difference being stated and these have to be found. For example, we may wish to find the tenth term of the A.P. which starts: $3\frac{1}{4}$, $5\frac{1}{2}$, $7\frac{3}{4}$, . . . The first term is $3\frac{1}{4}$ and to find the common difference notice that any term is obtained from the preceding one by adding on the common difference. Hence any two successive terms will differ by the common difference. In this case take $5\frac{1}{2}$ and subtract $3\frac{1}{4}$ to obtain the common difference. If you are using your calculator you will have to change the problem into decimals, of course, and take 3·25 from 5·5; the answer is 2·25.

The tenth term is required. With an A.P. we start with the first term and add one common difference to obtain the second term. To find the third term we add another common difference making two in all. Similarly the fourth term will be the first term with three common differences added on. And so on. Hence the tenth term will be the first term with nine common differences added on.

There are various ways of dealing with this on the calculator. We may enter the common difference, 2·25, multiply by 9, then add the first term (3·25). If your machine has a constant operating on addition, enter 2·25 as the constant, then 3·25 (the first term) into your display. Now press the addition key nine times. The tenth term is 23·5.

Many examples on series require us to find the sum of a specified number of terms of the series. For instance, instead of finding the tenth term of the series in the example above, we may be required to find the sum of the first ten terms. If your calculator has a memory proceed as follows:

Set 2·25 as the constant factor.

Enter 3·25 into the display and add to the memory.

Press the + Key, followed by M+.

Repeat the last line so that you have done it nine times in all.

Press RM.

The answer will be 133·75.

Note the following points. If your calculator has an automatic accumulator, there is no necessity to press the M+ key each time. As soon as 3·25 has been added to the memory,

press the accumulator key so that each time you press the +
key to produce the next term, it will be automatically added to
the memory.

Also notice that as you are pressing the + key you are
generating the terms of the series, so that the display immediately before you press RM should show the tenth term of the
series which we had previously calculated as 23·5.

If your calculator has not got a memory, you could do the
work by generating each of the ten terms, noting them on paper
and finally adding the terms as written down.

However, try this! Enter the first term of the series into
your calculator, add the last term and multiply your answer by
half the number of terms, i.e.

Enter 3·25

Add 23·5

Multiply result by 5 (i.e. half of ten terms)

Compare your answer with that obtained by the earlier method.

How does this work? Start with the first ten terms which
you obtained earlier and write them down like this:

3·25	23·5
5·5	21·25
7·75	19
10	16·75
12·25	14·5

In each line we have paired the first and the last, the second
and the next to the last, the third and the third from the end,
etc. Now add the numbers on each of the lines and compare
your five answers. So the sum of the ten terms may be obtained
by adding the first and the last terms and multiplying the
result by half the number of terms. This may be written as a
formula. If a is the first term, l the last term and n the number
of terms, then the sum S is given by

$$S = \frac{n}{2}(a + l)$$

Also if we call the common difference d, the first term is a, the second is a + d, the third is a + 2d, the fourth is a + 3d and so on. The nth term (where n is any number) would be a + (n − 1)d. This is the last term of the series, if there are n terms in the series, and is denoted by *l* in the formula above. Substituting this value for *l*, a second formula is obtained for the sum of n terms of an A.P.

$$S = \frac{n}{2}[a + a + (n - 1)\,d]$$

or better $\qquad S = \frac{n}{2}[2a + (n - 1)\,d]$

Notice that with this formula we do not need to know the last term. Try the example above once more, this time given that the first term is 3·25, the number of terms is 10 and the common difference is 2·25.

Examples

(1) Find the sum of a series with twelve terms, first term 8, common difference 1·7.

In this case n = 12, a = 8 and d = 1·7.

Proceed with your calculator as follows:

Enter	*Display represents*
12	n
−1	n − 1
× by 1·7	(n − 1)d
Add 8 twice	2a + (n − 1)d
× by 12	n[2a + (n − 1)d]
÷ by 2	S

The result is 208·2.

(2) Find the sum of all the numbers between 200 and 400 which are divisible by 7.

Enter 200 in your calculator; divide by 7; answer 28·571428.

Hence the first number above 200 which is divisible by 7 will be 29 × 7, i.e. 203.

Similarly find the last number *below* 400 which is divisible by 7. Your answer should be 399.

Subtract 203 from 399. Divide the result by 7. Answer 28. This means that starting at 203, there are 28 common differences of 7 added to obtain the last term. From the results above it follows that there must be 29 terms including both 203 and 399. So that the problem is really asking for the sum of the A.P. whose first term is 203, the last term is 399 and the number of terms is 29. Use the formula and calculator as follows:

Add 203 and 399; multiply result by 29; divide by 2. (Alternatively, using the second formula with d = 7, multiply 28 by 7; add 203 twice; multiply the result by 29 and finally divide by 2.) The result is 8729.

Examples to try:

14a Write down eight terms of the series with:
   (i) first term 5·2 and common difference 2·25
   (ii) first term 4·6 and common difference − 1·4
   (iii) first term 128 and common difference 17.

14b Sum the series:
   (i) 3·5, 4·7, 5·9, . . . to ten terms.
   (ii) 12, 18, 24, . . . to 30 terms
   (iii) 8·6, 6·4, 4·2, . . . to 12 terms.

14c Find the sum of all numbers between 151 and 350 which are divisible by 6.

Geometric progressions

If we obtain a series of numbers by multiplying successive terms by the same amount, the result is a geometric progression. As an example we may start with the number 2 and multiply each time by 3 to obtain the geometric progression (G.P.):

   2, 6, 18, 54, 162, 486, . . .

In this type of progression the number by which we multiply each time (in the above case 3) is called the common ratio. For any given G.P. we can find the common ratio by dividing any term by the preceding term. Thus in the G.P. 8, 12, 18, ... the common ratio is obtained by dividing 12 by 8, i.e. $\frac{12}{8}$ or 1·5.

Strictly speaking we could have a common ratio where we were dividing by the same number each time. For example in the series 24, 12, 6, 3, ... we are dividing each successive term by 2 in order to obtain the next term. However this is equivalent to multiplying by $\frac{1}{2}$, so in practice we only consider the process as multiplying by the common ratio, noting that it could be less than 1. Unfortunately in the case of calculator usage this can lead to slight errors, so results where the ratio is less than 1 should be looked at carefully. As an example, suppose the common ratio is $\frac{1}{3}$ and the first term is 324.

Enter 3 as your constant, then put 324 in the display.

Press the division key repeatedly and the following series is obtained (if your machine does not have a constant key, simply divide by 3 repeatedly):

324, 108, 36, 12, 4, ...

Next repeat the exercise but instead of dividing by 3, multiply by $\frac{1}{3}$. Mathematically this is exactly the same process, but since calculators work in decimals and $\frac{1}{3}$ is a non-terminating decimal, we obtain some strange results!

One-third is 0·333333 . . . so enter this number into your machine with as many threes as the capacity will allow and transfer this to the constant. Now enter 324 and press the multiplication key repeatedly. You will obtain a series somewhat as follows:

324, 107·99998, 35·999989, 11·999995, 3·999979, . . .

Notice that because 0·3333333 is not exactly one-third, the terms after the first are close, but not exactly the true values as found in the first working of the problem. Whenever you see numbers such as 107·99998 which differ from a whole number by a very small amount (in this case only 0·00002) investigate them carefully since the true value may be the whole number.

In the case of a G.P. the first term usually is denoted by the letter a and the common ratio by the letter r. So if the series starts with a, the second term will be ar, the third term will be ar^2, the fourth term ar^3 and so on. Hence to obtain any term we simply multiply the first term by the common ratio for a given number of times and that number of times is always one less than the number of terms. If we require the twelfth term it will mean multiplying the first term by the common ratio eleven times.

Examples

(1) Find the eighth and tenth terms of the series whose first term is 4 and common ratio 2·25.

Enter 4 in your calculator and multiply by 2·25 seven times to obtain the first answer and nine times to obtain the second answer (use the constant key if you have one). The answers are 1167·7169 and 5911·5667 (to the capacity of an eight-digit machine).

(2) Find the first term of a G.P. whose third term is 18 and whose fifth term is $40\frac{1}{2}$.

The fifth term will be obtained from the third term by multiplying it by the common ratio twice.

Use your calculator to divide 40·5 by 18. The answer is 2·25. This represents r^2. There is no need to work out r itself in this case, since the third term will be ar^2, i.e. the first term multiplied by the common ratio twice. So to obtain the first term, a, divide the third term by r^2, i.e. by 2·25. Doing this on your calculator you obtain 8 as your answer.

Work out on your calculator successive terms of the G.P.

whose first term is 3 and common ratio 5. The G.P. starts 3, 15, 75, 375, 1875, . . . and you can continue for some time but eventually reach the capacity of your calculator and can go no further. However, if we had larger and larger calculators we could go on adding further terms indefinitely. But no calculator, however large its capacity, could find the last term of the series; the numbers just go on for ever. We say that the series continues to infinity. In such a series, since the terms are getting larger each time, the sum of the terms of the series will be infinitely large. Such a series is said to diverge.

Now use your calculator to generate successive terms of the series whose first term is 12 and common ratio 0·1. The first few terms are 12, 1·2, 0·12, 0·012, . . . Eventually your calculator will register 0. This does not mean that the value of that particular term is zero, but that the term is so small that it is beyond the capacity of your calculator. If we are finding the sum of a G.P. in such a case, then as we add successive terms the amount that is being added soon becomes almost negligible and has little effect on the sum. If we keep within the capacity of an eight-digit calculator for the series above, the eighth term is 0·0000012 which is negligible compared with the sum of the first two terms only! A G.P. of this type is said to be convergent and in such cases it is possible to find the sum of an infinite number of terms.

The sum of the terms of a G.P. may be obtained on a calculator by generating successive terms and summing them; this is particularly easy if the machine has a memory.

Example

Find the sum of ten terms of the series 3, 6, 12, etc.

Obviously a = 3 and r = 2.

Enter 2 as constant.

Put 3 in the display and multiply repeatedly by the constant, adding each term to the memory. If your machine does not have a memory, jot down the terms on paper and add later. (If you are using the memory, don't forget to add the first term, 3). The total for the ten terms is 3069.

In mathematical texts a formula is proved for the sum of a given number of terms of a G.P. It can be written in one of the forms:

$$S = a\,\frac{r^n - 1}{r - 1} \qquad \text{or} \qquad S = a\,\frac{1 - r^n}{1 - r}$$

where S represents the sum, a, the first term, r, the common ratio and n the number of terms. The first version of the formula is used when r is greater than 1, the second when r is less than 1.

Taking the example above, we would use the formula given first and the sum of ten terms will be given by

$$S = 3 \times \frac{2^{10} - 1}{2 - 1}$$

A calculator is not needed to work out the denominator which is equal to 1. So use your calculator to find 2^{10}, subtract 1 and multiply the result by 3.

Examples to try

14d Find the sum of eight terms of the G.P. whose first term is 1 and common ratio 4.

14e Find the sum of six terms of the G.P. $12 + 6 + 3 + \ldots$ (Here the common ratio is $0\cdot5$, so use the second version of the formula.)

14f The first term of a G.P. is 4 and the third term is 25. Find the common ratio and the sum of six terms. (You will need to find a square root – see next chapter).

Sum to infinity

To find the sum to six terms of the series $4 + 0\cdot8 + 0\cdot16 + \ldots$, we would divide the second term by the first to obtain the common ratio, $0\cdot2$, and use the formula

$$S = 4 \times \frac{1 - (0 \cdot 2)^6}{1 - 0 \cdot 2}$$

$$= 4 \times \frac{1 - 0 \cdot 000064}{0 \cdot 8}$$

$$= 4 \cdot 99968$$

Notice how very small $0 \cdot 2^6$ is. If you use your calculator to find powers of $0 \cdot 2$ you will find that it becomes too small for your calculator to handle after the tenth power (assuming an eight-digit calculator). And if we take an infinite number of terms, the terms become infinitely small, i.e. zero. For an infinite series, therefore, the term r^n becomes zero and the formula for the sum to infinity is

$$S = \frac{a}{1 - r}.$$

For the series we have just been considering, the sum to infinity will be $\frac{4}{1 - 0 \cdot 2} = 5$. The idea can be valuable in certain calculations.

Example

A ball is dropped from an initial height of 10 feet. Each time it hits the ground it rebounds to a height of two-thirds the height from which it fell. How far does it travel before coming to rest?

First fall = 10 feet.

Height of second fall = height of first rebound = $\frac{2}{3} \times 10$ feet.

Height of third fall = height of second rebound = $\frac{2}{3} \times \frac{2}{3} \times 10$ feet.

and so on.

The total distance is given by

$$10 + 2 \left[\tfrac{2}{3} \times 10 + (\tfrac{2}{3})^2 \times 10 + \ldots \right]$$

Note: (a) we multiply the terms by 2 to obtain the distance up and down.

(b) We assume the bouncing continues indefinitely, although it will soon become imperceptible; hence we sum the G.P. to infinity.

We can simplify the expression for the distance to become

$$10 + 20 \left(\tfrac{2}{3} + (\tfrac{2}{3})^2 + (\tfrac{2}{3})^3 + \ldots \text{ to infinity} \right)$$

$$= 10 + 20 \times \frac{0 \cdot 6666666}{0 \cdot 3333333} = 50 \text{ feet.}$$

(1st term = $\tfrac{2}{3}$; common ratio = $\tfrac{2}{3}$; substitute formula for S above within outside brackets)

Examples to try

14g A spring under compression shrinks 3 cm. in the first second of time and in subsequent seconds by 0·6 of what it shrank in the previous second. Find the total shrinkage.

14h Find the sum to infinity of the series
3·2, 1·6, 0·8, ...

Compound interest law

Earlier in this book the idea of compound interest was explained (Chapter 7). It was also shown that the simple interest on a principal of £P for T years at R per cent per annum was

$$£\frac{PRT}{100}.$$

Hence the interest for one year is $£\dfrac{PR}{100}$ and the amount at the end of the year is $£\, P + \dfrac{PR}{100}$ or $£\, P \left(1 + \dfrac{R}{100}\right)$.

In the case of compound interest, the interest for any year is calculated on the amount at the beginning of that year, so for the second year it will be calculated on a principal of $£\, P \left(1 + \dfrac{R}{100}\right)$, which we will call P_2. The amount at the end of the second year, therefore will be $P_2 (1 + \frac{R}{100})$ by a calculation similar to that for the first year. By substituting the value of P_2, this amount will be £ $P (1 + \frac{R}{100}) (1 + \frac{R}{100})$ or £ $P (1 + \frac{R}{100})^2$.

In a similar manner the amount at the end of the third year will be £ $P (1 + \frac{R}{100})^3$ and more generally, the amount at the end of n years will be £ $P (1 + \frac{R}{100})^n$.

This proves the formula which was previously stated in Chapter 7 and the reason for proving it at this stage is to help the reader to understand what is happening in the case of compound interest: a quantity – in this case money – is being increased by a fixed percentage of what it was at the beginning of each year. The word "quantity" was used because other things beside money may be governed by the rule which we call "Compound Interest Law".

As an example consider a city with a population of 1·2 million people which has an annual population growth rate of 3·5 per cent and calculate what the population will be in ten years' time. Notice that the increase in any year is 3·5 per cent of what it was at the beginning of that year, so apply the compound interest formula:

$$\text{Population after ten years} = 1200000 (1\cdot035)^{10}$$
$$= 1692718$$

(Calculation method: set 1·035 as constant, enter 1200000 in display and multiply by the constant ten times.)

Remembering what was said in Chapter 13 and the fact that 1·2 million would be a round figure, we would give the population in ten years' time as 1·7 million.

It should be clear now that Compound Interest Law is another example of geometric series. We are not concerned with summing the series, but with finding the value of a particular term. The tenth term in a geometrical progression whose first term is 1200000 and whose common ratio is 1·035 is 1200000 $(1·035)^{10}$. Which is exactly what was obtained in the above example on population.

Compound interest law may be applied equally well to a quantity which is decreasing at a steady rate. The example earlier of a ball which was dropped from a height of ten feet and rebounded each time it hit the ground to a height which was two-thirds of the height from which it fell may be extended: find the height to which it rises after five impacts with the floor.

Notice that only one height is required and not the total distance as before. The initial distance is 10 and the common ratio is 0·6666666, so the height after the fifth bounce will be

$$10 \times (0·6666666)^5$$

This comes to 1·32 feet (to two decimal places). In this example the common ratio may not appear to be the same as the percentage increase rate which we applied in the case of compound interest, but the problem may be rephrased as follows:

A ball falls initially from a height of ten feet and after each impact with the ground it rises to a height which is $33\frac{1}{3}$ per cent less than the height from which it fell. Using the formula $P(1 + \dfrac{R}{100})^n$, $P = 10$ and $n = 5$. Since the percentage is a loss and not a gain we change the sign from + to − and our formula becomes

$$10 \left(1 - \frac{33\frac{1}{3}}{100}\right)^5$$

or $10 (1 - 0·3333333)^5$, giving $10 \times (0·6666666)^5$ and the result as before.

Examples to try

14i A water plant grows so that the surface area of the water which it covers is increased each day by 5 per cent of what it was at the end of the previous day. If initially it covered 0·5 of a square metre, what area does it cover after 15 days?

14j Radioactive material disintegrates at a yearly rate which is a constant percentage of its radioactivity in the previous year. This means that it never fully loses its radioactivity and the time for it to become inactive cannot be calculated. The term "half-life" is used to describe the time of decay measured over the period in which it loses half of its radioactivity. This varies for different elements; for example radium has a half-life of 1580 years. Strontium 90 is present in the fall-out of hydrogen bomb explosions. Its annual rate of decay is 3·42 per cent of what its radioactivity was the previous year. Calculate the half-life of Strontium 90.

Other series

There are various well-known number sequences which can be calculated easily on the electronic calculator. A simple sequence of numbers is one based on a formula such as

$$x_{n+1} = x_n k + m$$

where k and m are constants and x_n represents the nth term in the sequence and x_{n+1} the $(n+1)$th term. This may seem complicated but simply means that to calculate the next term from the previous term you multiply the previous term by the number k and add the number m. A simple example would be

$$x_{n+1} = x_n (1·2) + 1.$$

If a particular term was 7·6, we obtain the next term of the sequence by multiplying 7·6 by 1·2 and adding 1. Having obtained this term, the following term may be found by repeating the process and so on.

The *Binomial Series* is the sequence of numbers which are the coefficients of the terms in the expansion of $(1 + x)^n$. The expansion may be written as follows:

$$(1 + x)^n = 1 + nx + \frac{n(n-1)}{1 \times 2}x^2 + \frac{n(n-1)(n-2)}{1 \times 2 \times 3}x^3 + \ldots$$

$$\ldots + \frac{n(n-1)(n-2)\ldots(n-r+1)}{1 \times 2 \times 3 \times \ldots \times r}x^r + \ldots + x^n$$

As a simple example we may take the case of $(1 + x)^4$ and note how the terms are evaluated.

$$(1 + x)^4 = 1 + 4x + \frac{4 \times 3}{1 \times 2}x^2 + \frac{4 \times 3 \times 2}{1 \times 2 \times 3}x^3 + \frac{4 \times 3 \times 2 \times 1}{1 \times 2 \times 3 \times 4}x^4$$

$$= 1 + 4x + 6x^2 + 4x^3 + x^4$$

There are two points to notice: (a) the coefficient of each term is obtained from the previous one by multiplying by a number and dividing by another number, e.g. x^3 from x^2 by multiplying the coefficient of x^2 by 2 and dividing by 3; (b) the terms decrease in the same way in which they increase, so that we need only evaluate about half the coefficients. (Also note that for the work here, we are restricting ourselves to the case where n is a positive whole number.)

It is possible to use the calculator to obtain the binomial terms very easily. Suppose that we wish to generate the terms of the Binomial expansion of $(1 + x)^{20}$, we may tabulate the results as follows and the method becomes clear:

Coefficient	*Operate on previous term*	*Term*
		1
20	$\times\ 20$	$20x$
$\dfrac{20 \times 19}{1 \times 2}$	$\times\ 19 \div 2$	$190x^2$
$\dfrac{20 \times 19 \times 18}{1 \times 2 \times 3}$	$\times\ 18 \div 3$	$1140x^3$
	$\times\ 17 \div 4$	$4845x^4$
	$\times\ 16 \div 5$	$15504x^5$
	etc.	

In practice, tabulation is not necessary since the operations are so simple to repeat that they may be fed into the calculator continuously and the terms written down as they are produced.

15

SOLUTIONS BY SUCCESSIVE APPROXIMATION

If asked to find x, which is a number such that $x + 3 = 7$, most people would readily answer that x was 4. If we made the problem a little harder by saying that $x + 3 \cdot 62849 = 7 \cdot 15472$ the method of finding the answer is the same: it is only the calculation which has become more difficult although that is performed easily if a calculator is to hand. In both cases the answer would be absolutely accurate.

Unfortunately in mathematics we meet problems where we are unable to obtain an absolutely accurate answer. We have met already one or two examples of these in earlier chapters. Thus one-third as a decimal is $0 \cdot 33333 \ldots$ and no matter how many threes we write we never get an accurate result. However, the more threes we take, the nearer we approach the actual value of one-third.

This is a simple example since all that is needed to obtain greater accuracy is to add another figure three to the end of the existing answer. But there are problems in mathematics which are similar although finding more accurate solutions is rather more difficult.

Square roots
The square root of a number is that quantity which when multiplied by itself gives us the number. For example, the square root of nine is three, since three multiplied by itself gives nine. Similarly the square root of 16 is 4, the square root

of 36 is 6 and the square root of 81 is 9. What happens if we require the square root of a number such as 5? Two multiplied by itself is 4, and three multiplied by itself is 9. Since 5 lies between 4 and 9, the square root of 5 must lie between 2 and 3. Unfortunately it is one of those numbers which never works out accurately, so how do we find a reasonably close answer?

One method which we can use is to find an approximate solution, then use this to obtain a second approximation which is more accurate than the first. The process may be repeated so that we obtain a third approximation which is more accurate than the second. We may go on like this until we obtain the degree of accuracy that we desire. Unfortunately some of the calculations involved are rather difficult although the method itself is fairly simple, but now that calculators and computers have become available to undertake the calculations these methods are used much more than they were in the past. The machines have taken the hard slog out of the process and have speeded up a long and tedious series of operations. The method used is called *iteration* and certain problems will now be solved using these iterative methods.

Returning to the problem of finding the square root of 5, it was stated that the solution must lie between 2 and 3, so take 2·5 as a first approximation. If 2·5 is the correct answer, then when we divide 5 by 2·5 we should obtain 2·5 again. In other words, since 2·5 × 2·5 would have to equal 5, then 5 ÷ 2·5 would have to equal 2·5. Doing this division

$$\frac{5}{2 \cdot 5} = 2.$$

Clearly the answer is incorrect, but it does show that the estimate of 2·5 was too high and that we should have made an estimate somewhere between 2·5 and 2. As we are not certain just where it lies between these two, a useful guess would be half-way, i.e. 2·25. We therefore take 2·25 as the second approximation and repeat the process. So far we have been doing the working in our heads but now the numbers are becoming more difficult and we shall have to use the calculator. Also it would be useful if the working was set out in tabular form. Start on the top line and work across: at the end of a line, the new approximation is transferred to the start of the next line. Check the working of each line on your own calculator.

Approximation (call this x)	$\dfrac{5}{x}$	$\frac{1}{2}(x + \dfrac{5}{x})$
2·5	2	2·25
2·25	2·2222222	2·2361111
2·2361111	2·2360248	2·2360679
2·2360679	2·2360680	2·2360679

Since we have obtained the same answer on two successive lines this is the greatest accuracy possible with the calculator and this last number represents the square root of 5 to that degree of accuracy, i.e. seven decimal places. In case you are uncertain about the formula $\frac{1}{2}(x + \dfrac{5}{x})$ at the head of the last column, remember that what we are doing here is to find a number half-way between the numbers in the first two columns since this will be closer to our desired answer than the approximation we have just used; hence the first two columns are added and half that value is taken.

The working was set out in this tabular form so that you could understand what was being done. If you did the working on your own calculator you probably discovered that much of this setting down was unnecessary. As a further example, the square root of 7 will be calculated but this time the actual operations on a non-memory machine will be given. The answer will be between 2 and 3, so take 2·5 as a first approximation.

	Display
Enter 7 and divide by 2·5	2·8
Add 2·5 and divide by 2	2·65
Write down 2·65	
Enter 7 and divide by 2·65	2·6415094
Add 2·65 and divide by 2	2·6457547
Write down 2·6457547	
Enter 7 and divide by 2·6457547	2·6457479
Add 2·6457547 and divide by 2	2·6457513
Write down 2·6457513	
Enter 7 and divide by 2·6457513	2·6457513

Since this is the same as the previous answer, we need not proceed further and the square root of 7 is 2·6457513.

With certain types of machine even less writing down is needed.

If your calculator has a constant key which works on all four functions and can be released, proceed as follows:

	Display
Enter 7 and divide by 2·5	2·8
Add 2·5 and divide by 2	2·65
Press K key	
Enter 7 and press divide key	2·6415094
Press + key and release K; divide by 2	2·6457547

Repeat last three lines as often as required.

If your calculator has a memory, proceed as follows:

	Display
Enter 7 and divide by 2·5	2·8
Add 2·5 and divide by 2	2·65
Press M+ key	
Enter 7, press divide key, then RM and =	2·6415094
Add contents of memory and divide by 2	2·6457547

Clear Memory and press M+ key.

Repeat last three steps as often as necessary. If clearing the memory on your machine causes you to lose the display, use the method given in Practical tip 2 at the end of Chapter 5.

Although it is not necessary to write down any intermediate results when using the constant key methods, a careful watch should be kept on the value of each approximation so that the process may be stopped when the values of two successive approximations are the same. Minimal writing down of the successive memory figures is needed using the memory method.

It is worth noting that when using methods of successive approximation, the first approximation need not be very close and the final result would still be correct. For instance we could have started the last example by saying that the first approximation to the square root of 7 was 1. This is obviously not near the result, but we should have obtained the answer eventually. The nearer the first approximation is to the actual result, the fewer times we have to repeat the calculation and the sooner we obtain the answer. It is also worth noting that if an error is made at some point in the calculation, the correct answer will be obtained once more, though again it is likely to take you longer!

Examples to try

15a Find the square roots of the following numbers:

2, 3, 11, 152

15b Pythagoras' Theorem tells us that to find the length of the hypotenuse (i.e. the longest side) of a right-angled triangle, we square the lengths of each of the other two sides, add these squares together and find the square root of this sum. For example, if the two sides are 3 metres and 4 metres long as in fig. 9, we square these quantities and add them: $3^2 + 4^2 = 9 + 16 = 25$. The length of the hypotenuse will be the square root of 25, which is 5. Find the length of the hypotenuse of a right-angled

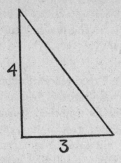

Fig. 9

triangle when the lengths of the other two sides are 10 metres and 12 metres.

15c Use Pythagoras' Theorem to find the length of the diagonal of a square lawn whose side measures 6 metres. (Hint: The diagonal will be the hypotenuse of a right-angled triangle whose sides are of what length?)

15d The foot of a ladder 16 feet long is 4 feet from the foot of the wall against which the ladder is leaning. How far up the wall is the top of the ladder? (Hint: If h is the height up the wall, $16^2 = h^2 + 4^2$, so $h^2 = 16^2 - 4^2$. Stop your working at an appropriate degree of accuracy.)

Solving equations by iteration

Iterative methods can be useful in finding the solution of equations which either have no exact solution or which cannot be solved easily by normal methods. A simple example is $x^2 + 3x - 1 = 0$. There are standard ways of solving this equation (see the next chapter for equations generally) but the actual solution is not an exact one, so we have to decide what degree of accuracy we require. In earlier examples of iteration we worked to the capacity of the machine, but suppose that in this case we only require an answer to four decimal places. This will illustrate how the calculation is stopped once the required degree of accuracy has been obtained.

The equation $x^2 + 3x - 1 = 0$ can be written as
$$3x = 1 - x^2 \text{ and dividing throughout by 3,}$$
as
$$x = \frac{1 - x^2}{3}$$

This is what is called a "recurrence relation" and if we substitute any value for x in the right-hand side of this relation, we obtain a value for x in the left-hand side. If the value of x substituted is the correct solution of the equation, then the right-hand side will have the same value. We could start with any value for x but it will save work if a value is chosen which is reasonably near the correct one.

If we put $x = 1$, $\dfrac{1 - x^2}{3}$ becomes zero.

If we put $x = 2$, it $= -1$

If we put $x = 3$, it $= -\dfrac{8}{3}$

The values of 1 and 0, then 2 and -1, and 3 and $-\dfrac{8}{3}$

show a widening gap when we need the two values to coincide, so we ought to proceed in the other direction, i.e. decrease the value of x. Put $x = 0$; we then find that the right-hand side is equal to $\frac{1}{3}$. This is a fairly close result, so take $x = 0$ as a first approximation. Once again tabulate the results:

x	$1 - x^2$	$\dfrac{1 - x^2}{3}$
0	1	0·3333333
0·3333333	0·8888890	0·2962963
0·2962963	0·9122086	0·3040695
0·3040695	0·9075418	0·3025139
0·3025139	0·9084854	0·3028284
0·3028284	0·9082950	0·3027650

We have been watching the figures in the last column and now notice that if we correct the last entry to four decimal places (i.e. rounding up) we obtain 0·3028 which is identical with the first four decimal places in the line above. Consequently this is our solution to four decimal places.

The method of key operation for the above example will not be described in detail since by now you are probably sufficiently familiar with your own machine to be able to tackle the calculations in the most convenient way. Notice that with some machines (especially those with a memory) much of the setting down is unnecessary.

Readers with some knowledge of mathematics will have noted that the solution of the equation $x^2 + 3x - 1 = 0$ given above is not the complete solution. A quadratic equation such as this has two values of x (or roots as they are called) for its complete solution. However, having obtained one root as 0·3028, the other is easily obtained. If p and q are the two roots of a quadratic equation represented by $ax^2 + bx + c = 0$ (where a, b and c are numbers), then $p + q = -\dfrac{b}{a}$ and $pq = \dfrac{c}{a}$. The proof of this will not be given here; it can be found in textbooks on algebra. Taking the equation $x^2 + 3x - 1 = 0$ and comparing it with $ax^2 + bx + c = 0$, we can obtain our equation from the latter by putting $a = 1$, $b = 3$ and $c = -1$. As further examples consider $5x^2 - 2x + 4 = 0$ and $2x^2 - 7 = 0$. In the first $a = 5$, $b = -2$ and $c = 4$; in the second $a = 2$, $b = 0$ (since there are no x's) and $c = -7$.

Returning to the original equation, where we found that $a = 1$, $b = 3$ and $c = -1$, we now know that if we add the two roots they come to -3 (obtained from $-\dfrac{b}{a}$) and if we multiply the two roots the answer is -1 (from $\dfrac{c}{a}$). It does not matter which of these two facts we use. If we take the first, since one root is 0·3028, the other will be $-3·3028$. If we take the

second fact, we know our other root will be $-\dfrac{1}{0.3028}$ and
working this out on the calculator we obtain -3.3025.

Some examples to try
15e Solve the equations (to 4 decimal places):
    (a) $2x^2 + 5x - 1 = 0$ (b) $x^2 - 4x - 2 = 0$

Limitations
A word of warning is necessary because sometimes the method
fails. This is due to the nature of the function and not to the
method of calculation. A brief explanation is given below but
if you do not wish to follow this, note what is stated in the
final paragraph since this will enable you to spot when the
method is not working.

  What we are doing when we use the method shown above is
to express the equation as two simultaneous equations. Thus in
the worked example we have obtained two equations: $y = x$ and
$y = \dfrac{1 - x^2}{3}$. If we consider the solution graphically, we have
two graphs as shown in fig. 10; the straight-line graph is $y = x$
and the curve is the other. The solution is where the two
intersect. First we gave x the value 0 and found $\dfrac{1 - x^2}{3}$
to obtain the value 0.3333333; this corresponds to where the
curve cuts the Y-axis (Point A). We now used this value of y to
obtain a new value of x (also 0.3333333, since $y = x$). We do
this on the diagram by drawing the horizontal line AB. With
this value of x we use our other equation $(y = \dfrac{1 - x^2}{3})$ to
obtain a new value for y. This is done on the graph by drawing
BC down from the straight line onto the curve; the new value
of y is the value of y at C. Again we use this to find the next

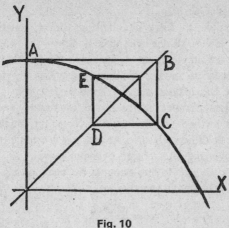

Fig. 10

value of x; on the diagram we draw CD. And so on. Looking at the diagram, it is clear that we are getting closer to the point of intersection of the straight line and the curve, which is the point which will give the true solution.

However in some cases the method fails because the lines AB, BC, CD, etc., which we drew on our graph do *not* encircle the true value and continually approach it. In fact just the opposite takes place and instead of getting nearer successively, we get further and further away from the desired value. We use the terms "converging" and "diverging". In our example, the values converged to the true value. With some other equations we may find the whole process diverges.

Returning to numerical work, therefore, we must watch what is happening to the successive approximations. As we get each new approximation to the required answer, it should be approaching some particular value. Look again at the examples we have done and you will see this happening. If, however, the successive approximations show gradually increasing differences or fluctuate wildly, then the method fails.

Other types of equation

It is possible to solve simultaneous linear equations by iteration, e.g. equations such as $x + y = 7$; $x + 4y = 6$. But there are simpler methods which take far less time. There are methods of solving quadratic equations by formulae which are less tedious than by iteration (see next chapter). Nevertheless iterative methods are interesting and often provide a method of solution of an equation which would otherwise be difficult to solve. An example is a cubic equation, i.e. one involving third powers of the unknown.

Suppose we wish to find a root of the equation $x^3 - 3x + 1 = 0$. Rearrange the equation as

$$x = \frac{x^3 + 1}{3}$$

A value of $x = 1$ appears to be a useful first approximation and the work is set down as follows:

x	$\dfrac{x^3 + 1}{3}$
1	0·6666666
0·6666666	0·4320987
0·4320987	0·3602256
0·3602256	0·3489145
0·3489145	0·3474924
0·3474924	0·3473200
0·3473200	0·3472991
0·3472991	0·3472966
0·3472966	0·3472963
0·3472963	0·3472963

Note that the easiest way to obtain x^3 is to enter the value of x, press the K key, then the multiplication key twice. This multiplies the value of x in the display by itself twice, which of course is x^3. If your machine enables you to release the constant, you complete the calculation by doing so, then adding

1 and dividing the result by 3. If your calculator does not allow you to release the constant, you may wish to add an intermediate column in the above table where you would write down the values of x^3. After clearing the machine, you could then use these values to find the corresponding values in the final column.

Examples to try

15f Find a root of the equation $x^3 - 5x + 2 = 0$.

15g Find a root of the equation $x^3 + 7x - 6 = 0$.

16

SOLVING EQUATIONS

This chapter is concerned largely with matters mathematical. A great deal of the mathematical background will be found in textbooks on algebra, but what follows will show how the electronic calculator may be used to solve equations of the types which appear in algebra textbooks. Moreover many of the examples which appear in such textbooks contain equations which are unrealistically simple so that they can be solved fairly easily, e.g. coefficients which are whole numbers. As you will have realized by now it does not matter to the calculator whether it has to deal with whole numbers or with numbers containing many places of decimals.

Types of equation

The simplest type of equation is a linear equation, so called because the graph, when drawn, appears as a straight line. Such equations contain first powers of the unknown only, such as $3x$, $4y$, $2z$, but *not* x^2, $3y^2$, z^3. Some examples of this type of equation are:

$$5x + 7 - 3x - 4 = x + 6 \tag{1}$$
$$3 \cdot 2y - 1 \cdot 7 = 1 \cdot 4y + 3 \cdot 5 \tag{2}$$
$$x + 3y = 5 \tag{3}$$
$$3x - 2y = 4 \tag{4}$$
$$x + 3y - z = 4 \tag{5}$$
$$2x - y + z = 3 \tag{6}$$
$$3x + y - 2z = -1 \tag{7}$$

Equation (1) is said to be a simple linear equation because it contains only one unknown, represented in this case by x.

These are the easiest equations to solve since they only require rearrangement with the terms involving x on one side and the terms free from x on the other. In this case we should arrange the equation as:

$$5x - 3x - x = 6 - 7 + 4$$

So $x = 3$

Equation (2) is also a simple linear equation. The only difference from equation (1) is that the coefficients are not whole numbers. This is also simple to solve; if the numbers are a little difficult to handle, the calculator will soon work them out. Equation (2) could be rewritten as:

$$3 \cdot 2y - 1 \cdot 4y = 3 \cdot 5 + 1 \cdot 7$$
$$1 \cdot 8y = 5 \cdot 2$$
$$y = \frac{5 \cdot 2}{1 \cdot 8} = 2 \cdot 9.$$

(Notice that the answer given by the calculator is $2 \cdot 8888888$ but we only give one decimal place since the equation involved only one decimal place in each of the numbers.)

Equations (3) and (4) above are also linear equations, but this time involve two unknowns, x and y. Generally speaking, if an equation involves two unknowns, then you must have another equation in order to be able to solve it. We might be given both equations (3) and (4) in the same problem and be asked to solve them. This means that we wish to find values for x and y which will solve the two equations at the same time (or simultaneously). Hence equations such as (3) and (4) are called simultaneous linear equations in two unknowns.

The general rule applies, that if you have two unknowns you need two equations to be able to solve them, if you have three unknowns you need three equations and so on. So equations (5), (6) and (7) could be three simultaneous linear equations in three unknowns.

We now come to equations which involve powers of the

unknown, i.e. x^2, $5x^3$, etc. The highest power of the unknown in any such equation determines its type and name.

$$3x^2 + 5x - 7 = 0 \tag{8}$$
$$x^3 - 2x^2 + 3x - 8 = 0 \tag{9}$$
$$2x^4 - x^3 + 2x - 3 = 0 \tag{10}$$

In equation (8) the term with the highest power of x is $3x^2$. An equation whose highest power of x is 2 is said to be a quadratic equation. The highest power of x in equation (9) is 3 and such an equation is called a cubic equation. In equation (10) the highest power of x is 4 and these equations are called quartic or bi-quadratic. We can use a different terminology and describe an equation such as (10) as a fourth degree equation. This is the description we tend to apply to equations involving higher powers than the fourth, e.g. a fifth degree equation has highest power of x^5.

The electronic calculator will now be used to solve equations of different types.

Simultaneous linear equations

The solution of simple linear equations such as (1) and (2) above need not concern us here. As has been shown, solution is simply a matter of rearrangement. If this is not understood, a textbook on elementary algebra will soon make the process clear. There are a few different methods of solving simultaneous linear equations in two unknowns, but the method to be employed here starts with a method of solution known to most people who have done a little algebra. Taking the equations above:

$$x + 3y = 5 \tag{3}$$
$$3x - 2y = 4 \tag{4}$$

we need to eliminate either x or y from these so that we obtain an equation involving only one of the unknowns. Multiply the first equation throughout by 3 to obtain

$$3x + 9y = 15$$
$$3x - 2y = 4$$

Subtracting $11y = 11$

Hence $y = 1$

Putting $y = 1$ in equation (3), $x + 3 = 5$, so $x = 2$.

We have now found the values of x and y which solve the two equations. You can check that these values are correct by substituting in equation (4).

This process will now be repeated with two equations of a general nature.

$$ax + by + c = 0 \qquad\qquad (11)$$
$$dx + ey + f = 0 \qquad\qquad (12)$$

a, b, c, d, e and f represent numbers, positive or negative, and by giving these appropriate values, equations (11) and (12) may be made to represent any given simultaneous linear equations in two unknowns.

For example, putting $a = 1$, $b = 3$, $c = -5$, $d = 3$, $e = -2$, $f = -4$, we obtain equations (3) and (4). Notice the negative values -5 and -4 since we have moved the numbers 5 and 4 of equations (3) and (4) to the left-hand side to correspond with the positions of c and f.

In order to eliminate x from equations (3) and (4) it was necessary to have the coefficients of x in the two equations with the same value; they were both made equal to 3. We can do this with equations (11) and (12) by multiplying by d in (11) and by a in (12), thus:

$$adx + bdy + cd = 0$$
$$adx + aey + af = 0$$

In subtracting, it will be more useful later to take the top line from the bottom and obtain:

$$(ae - bd)y + (af - cd) = 0$$

So

$$(ae - bd)y = -(af - cd)$$

and

$$y = -\frac{af - cd}{ae - bd}$$

The process may be repeated to eliminate y and obtain x.

$$aex + bey + ce = 0$$
$$bdx + bey + bf = 0$$

Subtracting the bottom line from the top:

$$(ae - bd)x + (ce - bf) = 0$$

and

$$(ae - bd)x = -(ce - bf)$$
$$(ae - bd)x = -ce + bf$$

So

$$x = \frac{bf - ce}{ae - bd}$$

Refer back to equations (11) and (12) and note how these two results may be written down immediately from the equations by applying a simple rule. In each case the denominator is obtained by taking the four coefficients of x and y as they are printed and multiplying across diagonally.

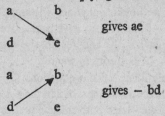

Notice the negative sign when the arrow is pointing upwards. The same rule applies in the case of the numerators but here we omit the coefficients for the unknown which we are finding; thus when we are finding x we do not use a and d.

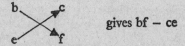

And when we are finding y we do not use b and e.

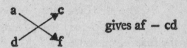

gives af — cd

One additional rule: in the case of y we make the whole result negative.

To test the result we can apply the rules to equations (3) and (4) above. Notice that we have to rewrite the equations to equal zero, thus:

$$x + 3y - 5 = 0$$
$$3x - 2y - 4 = 0$$

The denominators in each case will be $1 \times (-2) - 3 \times 3 = -11$.

The numerator for x will be $(3 \times -4) - (-2 \times -5) = -12 - 10 = -22$

So $x = \dfrac{-22}{-11} = 2$

The numerator for y will be $(1 \times -4) - (3 \times -5) = -4 + 15 = 11$

So $y = -\dfrac{11}{-11} = 1$

These are the same as the results obtained earlier.

The method just given may be applied to equations which call for the use of the calculator to obtain a solution. Equations are not always so simple as those printed in elementary algebra textbooks!

Example: Find x and y for the simultaneous equations
$$5 \cdot 21x + 0 \cdot 43y = 8 \cdot 13$$
$$9 \cdot 24x + 2 \cdot 37y = 10 \cdot 53$$

Rewriting the equations

$$5{\cdot}21x + 0{\cdot}43y - 8{\cdot}13 = 0$$
$$9{\cdot}24x + 2{\cdot}37y - 10{\cdot}53 = 0$$

We may write down expressions for x and y by inspection and application of the rules given above.

$$x = \frac{(0{\cdot}43 \times -10{\cdot}53) - (2{\cdot}37 \times -8{\cdot}13)}{(5{\cdot}21 \times 2{\cdot}37) - (9{\cdot}24 \times 0{\cdot}43)}$$

$$y = -\frac{(5{\cdot}21 \times -10{\cdot}53) - (9{\cdot}24 \times -8{\cdot}13)}{(5{\cdot}21 \times 2{\cdot}37) - (9{\cdot}24 \times 0{\cdot}43)}$$

Using a calculator to evaluate these,

$$x = \frac{14{\cdot}7402}{8{\cdot}3745} = 1{\cdot}76$$

(The numerator and denominator are written down separately before final evaluation since we are going to use the latter again for y)

$$y = -\frac{20{\cdot}2599}{8{\cdot}3745} = -2{\cdot}42$$

You may easily check if these answers are correct by substituting for x and y in either of the two original equations.

Examples to try

16a Solve the simultaneous equations $6x + 5y - 17 = 0$
$$8x - 3y + 12 = 0$$

16b Solve the simultaneous equations
$$6{\cdot}17x + 2{\cdot}3y = 9{\cdot}11$$
$$3{\cdot}54x + 1{\cdot}92y = 3{\cdot}99$$

There are similar methods for solving simultaneous equations in more than two unknowns, e.g. in three unknowns as in equations (5), (6) and (7) at the start of the chapter. However the methods are rather too long to be explained in detail here. The method used above depends on what are known as "determinants" and anyone wishing to take the matter further should look up this work in an advanced algebra book.

Nested multiplication

So far we have dealt with the solution of linear equations. Equations which involve higher powers of x and y (or whatever letters we are using) require different techniques. Before dealing with these, however, it is useful to note a method of finding the value of an algebraic expression when given the value of the unknown, which does not involve the use of a memory on the calculator or the writing down of intermediate answers.

Suppose we require the value of $2x^3 + 5x^2 - 3x + 7$ when x has the value $4 \cdot 61$. By straightforward substitution we should take the first term, $2x^3$, and multiply $4 \cdot 61$ by itself twice (with or without the use of the constant facility); then multiply the result by 2. We now need to make a fresh start with $5x^2$, multiplying $4 \cdot 61$ by itself and the result by 5. Note that we cannot do this without removing the result for $2x^3$ from the working part of the machine. In the case of a calculator with a memory, we could store it there; alternatively we have to write down the value of $2x^3$.

Similarly when we have found $5x^2$ we must add it to the memory or write it down before proceeding to calculate $3x$. In the end, of course, the results of the various calculations are added together (or subtracted in a case such as $-3x$).

An example of this type was worked fully at the end of Chapter 5. However, the use of a little algebra can restructure the expression so that it can be calculated by continuous entry into a calculator, without the need to use a calculator memory or write down intermediate answers.

Taking the expression above we may re-write it as follows:

$$2x^3 + 5x^2 - 3x + 7 = x(2x^2 + 5x - 3) + 7$$
$$= x[x(2x + 5) - 3] + 7$$

Start at the innermost bracket with substitution for x and it becomes possible to evaluate the expression by continuous entry. The method is tabulated below but you should compare each step with the last expression so that it is fully understood in what order the terms of the expression are brought into the calculation.

Term	Number and operation	Display	Terms in display
x	Enter 4·61	4·61	x
2x	× 2	9·22	2x
5	+ 5	14·22	2x + 5
x	× 4·61	65·5542	x(2x + 5)
3	− 3	62·5542	x(2x + 5) − 3
x	× 4·61	288·37486	x[x(2x + 5) − 3]
7	+ 7	295·37486	Expression

The value to two decimal places would be 295·37.

The example given in Chapter 5 when the use of the memory was being illustrated was $5x^3 + 3x^2 - 7x + 1$. To do this example in the manner illustrated above, we would write the expression as:

$$x[x(5x + 3) - 7] + 1$$

Try to evaluate this when $x = 4·7$ and compare your answer with that in Chapter 5.

Examples to try

N.B. In case of difficulty the factorization (restructuring the equation) in each case will be found in the answers at the back of the book.

16c Find the value of $3x^3 + 5x - 1$ when $x = 0·23$

16d Find the value of $4x^3 - 2x^2 + 3x + 2$ when $x = 1·4$.

Quadratic equations

The general quadratic equation is

$$ax^2 + bx + c = 0$$

where a, b and c are positive or negative constants. By giving appropriate values to these, the equation above can be made to represent any given quadratic equation. Thus if we have the equation $3x^2 - 2x + 1 = 0$, the corresponding values of a, b and c are 3, -2 and 1 respectively. Elementary algebra texts contain the proof that the solution of the general quadratic equation is

$$x = \frac{-b \pm \sqrt{(b^2 - 4ac)}}{2a}.$$

If the solution was required of the equation $3x^2 - 13x - 10 = 0$, we note that $a = 3$, $b = -13$ and $c = -10$ and substitute in the formula.

$$x = \frac{13 \pm \sqrt{(169 + 120)}}{6}$$

$$= \frac{13 \pm \sqrt{289}}{6}$$

Since the square root of 289 is 17, $x = \dfrac{13 \pm 17}{6}$

Taking the positive sign $\qquad x = \dfrac{30}{6} = 5$

Taking the negative sign $\qquad x = \dfrac{-4}{6} = -\dfrac{2}{3}$

There are two points to note. Firstly, there are various methods of solving quadratic equations and most people who are aware of these would have solved this particular equation much more simply by factorization; the method is in all elementary algebra books. Secondly, not all quadratic equations have real solutions, i.e. solutions which have a real meaning. For example, at the start of this section we gave an equation $3x^2 - 2x + 1 = 0$, giving $a = 3$, $b = -2$ and $c = 1$. Substituting these values in the formula, we obtain

$$x = \frac{2 \pm \sqrt{(4 - 12)}}{6}.$$

It will be seen that the numbers in the brackets equal -8 and it is impossible to find the square root of a negative quantity; hence this equation has no real solution.

The calculation involved in finding the solution of quadratic equations by this method is not extensive or difficult. The hardest part is usually finding the square root. This can be obtained from mathematical tables or by the iterative method given in Chapter 15. Some calculators have an automatic square root which does the calculation at the touch of a key. If mathematical tables are used for finding the square root, they usually give only a four-figure answer, but this will probably provide a degree of accuracy to satisfy most users. Finding the square root on your calculator gives a much greater degree of accuracy if desired.

The following example involves finding the square root, which will be done by iteration.

Find, to six decimal places, the roots (values of x) for the equation

$$5x^2 + 13x + 7 = 0$$

The roots are given by $x = \dfrac{-13 \pm \sqrt{(169 - 140)}}{10}$

$$= \dfrac{-13 \pm \sqrt{29}}{10}$$

To evaluate $\sqrt{29}$, notice that $\sqrt{25} = 5$ and $\sqrt{36} = 6$, so take 5·5 as a first estimate.

First approx. (x)	$\dfrac{29}{x}$	$\frac{1}{2}(x + \dfrac{29}{x})$
5·5	5·2727272	5·3863635
5·3863635	5·3839663	5·3851645
5·3851645	5·3851651	5·3851645

Hence $\qquad x = \dfrac{-7\cdot6148355}{10}$ or $\dfrac{-18\cdot3851645}{10}$

$$= -0\cdot761484 \quad \text{or} \quad -1\cdot838516$$

(to 6 d.p.)

Examples to try

16e $\qquad 3x^2 + 11x + 5 = 0$

16f $\qquad 6\cdot2x^2 - 8\cdot9x - 1\cdot1 = 0$

Solving equations by iteration

At the end of the chapter on Solutions by Successive Approximations (Chapter 15), a section demonstrated how these methods could be applied to the solution of equations and it might prove useful to read that section again at this point. The method given there depends on rearranging the equation to obtain a *recurrence relation*. This gives the unknown, x say, in terms of an expression involving x, so that by taking an approximate value for the unknown, it can be substituted in the expression to obtain a closer approximation.

The main requirement of any method of numerical calculation of roots of an equation is the ability to obtain a solution fairly quickly. The number of times the calculation has to be repeated in order to obtain a closer approximation depends very much on two things: (a) obtaining a fairly close approximation in the first place and (b) having a recurrence relation which gives easy substitution. It should be noted that it is usually possible to obtain more than one relation from any one equation and deciding which to choose is not always easy. As an example of this, consider the equation $x^3 - 3x + 1 = 0$ which was solved in Chapter 15 by the use of the relation

$$x = \frac{x^3 + 1}{3}$$

We could have obtained two other relations as follows:

(1) $\qquad\qquad x^3 = 3x - 1$

$\qquad$ or $\quad x = {}^3\sqrt{(3x - 1)}$

(2) $\qquad\qquad x^3 - 3x = -1$

$\qquad\qquad\quad x(x^2 - 3) = -1$

$$x = \frac{-1}{x^2 - 3}$$

$\qquad$ or $\quad x = \frac{1}{3 - x^2}$

The recurrence relation chosen for this example in the earlier chapter was probably the easiest to handle when using the calculator, but it is worth noting that the relation in (2) above leads to a quicker final result. The relation in (1) above takes the longest since it converges to the final result more slowly and the number of repetitions of the substitutions is much greater.

The Newton-Raphson method

Another method of solving equations by iteration is the Newton-Raphson method. It depends on differential calculus and a proof of the method will be found in mathematical textbooks which include calculus. A knowledge of calculus is necessary, but a brief introductory note below may help those without that knowledge to understand how the method is used.

Elementary differentiation is achieved by use of the formula that the differential coefficient of x^n is nx^{n-1}. This applies equally to the individual terms of an expression. Using the notation that $f'(x)$ denotes the differential coefficient of an expression denoted by $f(x)$, we may list certain examples:

$f(x)$	$f'(x)$
x^5	$5x^4$
x^{10}	$10x^9$
x^3	$3x^2$
x	1
$5x$	5
$13x^2$	$26x$
$7x^4$	$28x^3$
$3x^3 + 13x^2$	$9x^2 + 26x$
$x^4 + 5x^2 - 3$	$4x^3 + 10x$

(N.B. The differential coefficient of any constant is zero)

$5x^2 - 6x + 4$	$10x - 6$

The differential coefficient represents the gradient of the tangent to a particular curve at any point on it. To take the last example above, the differential coefficient of $5x^2 - 6x + 4$ is $10x - 6$. If the curve $y = 5x^2 - 6x + 4$ is drawn, then the gradient of the tangent to the curve at the point $x = 2$, for example, is obtained by putting $x = 2$ in $10x - 6$, i.e. $20 - 6 = 14$. It is the use of this gradient which forms the basis of the Newton-Raphson method. The tangent whose gradient had been obtained is used to find a closer approximation to the root than the previous approximation.

Using the notation given above of $f(x)$ and $f'(x)$ and given that x_0 represents a first approximation and x_1 a second approximation to the value of x for the equation $f(x) = 0$, we then use the relation

$$x_1 = x_0 - \frac{f(x_0)}{f'(x_0)}$$

This may look complicated to the reader unfamiliar with mathematical notation, but an example will illustrate. Compare the example used in Chapter 15 to find a solution of

$$x^3 - 3x + 1 = 0$$

Here $f(x) = x^3 - 3x + 1$ and $f'(x) = 3x^2 - 3$.

Choose $x = 0.5$ as the first approximation and substitute:

$f(x_0) = 0.125 - 1.5 + 1 = -0.375$

$f'(x_0) = 0.75 - 3 = -2.25$

So a closer approximation x_1 is given by

$$x_1 = 0.5 - \frac{-0.375}{-2.25}$$

$$= 0.5 - 0.1666666$$

$$= 0.3333333$$

This may now be used as a second approximation in order to obtain the next approximation, and so on. This is set out in tabular form below:

x_0	$f'(x_0)$	$f(x_0)$	$\dfrac{f(x_0)}{f'(x_0)}$
0·5000000	−2·25	−0·375	0·1666666
0·3333333	−2·6666666	0·0370370	−0·0138888
0·3472221	−2·6383107	0·0001958	−0·0000742
0·3472963	−2·6381559	0·0000001	

(N.B. x_0 in line 3 is obtained from $0·3333333 - (-0·0138888)$ which equals $0·3333333 + 0·0138888$)

There is no point in proceeding further since, when the last value of $f(x_0)$ is divided it will be displayed as zero. Hence $0·3472963$ is a root of the equation.

There are a number of matters arising which are beyond the scope of this book. For example, most cubic equations (i.e. those involving x^3) will have three roots, so how do we obtain the other two? Also what happens when the method fails? And why should it fail? Such points are considered in mathematical textbooks; it is our main purpose here to show how the calculator may be used for the different calculations.

The methods of calculator operation by which we may do the calculations involved in obtaining the results in the table above will now be considered.

Firstly, assuming that a simple four-function calculator is being used, as soon as $f(x)$ and $f'(x)$ are obtained they should be written in a form suitable for nested multiplication. So in the present case we would write $f(x)$ as $x(x^2 - 3) + 1$. In this particular case $f'(x)$ required no further transformation and may be left as $3x^2 - 3$. Evaluation of the table would then proceed as follows:

Key(s)	Display	Term(s)
0·5	0·5	x
× 0·5	0·25	x^2
× 3	0·75	$3x^2$
− 3	− 2·25	$3x^2 - 3$ or $f'(x)$

Clear after making a note of the answer − 2·25

0·5	0·5	x
× 0·5	0·25	x^2
− 3	−2·75	$x^2 - 3$
× 0·5	−1·375	$x(x^2 - 3)$
+ 1	−0·375	$x(x^2 - 3) + 1$ or $f(x)$
÷ (−2·25)	0·1666666	$f(x_0)/f'(x_0)$

This last value is now subtracted from 0·5 to obtain the new value of x, 0·3333333. (In case of difficulty, subtract 0·5 from 0·1666666 and change the sign.) The process is now repeated with this new value of x as the starting value for x.

In the case of a calculator which has a memory, it would not be necessary to make a note of the intermediate answer, −2·25 above. In such a machine this would be transferred to the memory, the rest of the calculation performed and then the −2·25 recalled from the memory for the division at the end.

An alternative method of working in the case of a memory machine would be to use the memory to find the values of f(x) and f′(x). Thus for $x^3 - 3x + 1$, x^3 would be calculated first and stored in the memory. Next 3x would be calculated and the result subtracted from the memory. Finally 1 would be added to the memory, whose contents would now be f(x). This method means that it is not necessary to do nested multiplication. However it will not be possible to store the value of f′(x) while f(x) is being worked out and so it is necessary once more to write down intermediate answers.

Examples to try
16g Find the root of the equation $x^3 + 2x - 5 = 0$
16h Find a root of the equation $x^3 + x^2 + 10 = 0$

The foregoing is by no means a comprehensive account of numerical methods applied to the solution of equations. There are types of equations (e.g. in three unknowns) and methods of solution which have not been covered here. The electronic calculator is invaluable in much of this work. Details will be found in texts on algebra and particularly on numerical analysis.

ANSWERS TO EXERCISES

Some answers are rounded; others may vary in the last figures.

2a	18		
2b	10		
2c	6		
3a	5·6666666	3·35	8·6875
	15·416666	2·125	3·25
3b	$\dfrac{311}{1000}$	$5\dfrac{29}{100}$	$\dfrac{37}{1000}$
	$83\dfrac{613}{1000}$		
3c	421·25	2868·625	14·318178
	232·5		
3d	0·3	0·08	0·225
	0·15	0·0625	0·093
	0·6666666	1·15	1·04
	0·95		
3e	82·08	25	0·78
	£0·84	£0·06	£3·12
3f	£0·26	£0·37	£0·14
	£0·05		
3g	364	706·2	£20·70
	£16·43		
3h	286	149·8	£15·30
	£14·57		
3i	£25	£37·50	£87·50
	27·5 kg	82·5 kg	110 kg
3j	0·421875	2·6153846	0·0727272

3k 0·139423   0·0465465
3l 4·5553852   1·0511348
5a 61·605   550·8017   12407
    3801·6614
6a £294·57
6b £407·03
6c £8·78
6d £23·30 (if VAT is on the new price only)
6e £7·20
6f 13·79%   17·86%
6g £414·80   £8·18
6h £129·17   £7·42
6i The balance on Mar. 25 should be £183·68 and the final
    balance £156·06.
7a £635·25   £21·04
7b £288·50   £37
7c £168·75
7d £270·83
7e £90
7f 5 per cent
7g 2·5 years
7h 6·5 per cent
7i £562·07   £1082·46
7j £38·51   £770·44
7k £719·95
7l 9 years
7m £2426
7n 11¾ years
7o £0·80
8a £328·26
8b 14 per cent
8c £273·98
8d About 13½ years
8e £620·49

8f, g, h, i Figures by calculation are £34·20, £48·66, £92·28, £39·90 respectively, showing the discrepancies of 10p, 35p, 13p, 7p.

9a 62·34 yards   20·12 metres   22·00 miles
    64·37 km/hr.

9b 226·80 grammes   6·35 kg   18·18 litres
    4046·9 sq. m.

9c 16·7p

9d 20·4p

9e 4·23p

9f £2·69

9g 1476·90   138·34   1937
    62480

9h 252 lira to 1 guilder

9i 1·83 fr.

9j 37·8   23·3   73·9
    − 7.8

9k 104   185   44·6
    10·4

12a 32·3 sq. m.

12b 28·72 sq. m.   £168

12c Roughly 4½ lb. (4·522)

12d 37·8 sq. m.

13a approx. 90   107·33246
     approx. 3000   3201·7
     approx. 1600   1369
     approx. 16800   15120

13b 262·144 cc

14a (i) 5·2, 7·45, 9·7, 11·95, 14·2, 16·45, 18·7, 20·95
     (ii) 4·6, 3·2, 1·8, 0·4, −1·0, −2·4, −3·8, −5·2
     (iii) 128, 145, 162, 179, 196, 213, 230, 247

14b 89   2970   −42

14c 8316

14d 21845

14e 23·625

14f 2·5 648·375

14g 7·5 cm.

14h 6·4

14i 1·04 sq. m.

14j Just under 20 years (actually 19·9)

15a 1·4142135 1·7320508 3·3166247
12·328828

15b 15·62 metres

15c 8·49 metres

15d 15·49 feet

15e −2·6861, 0·1861
4·4495, −0·44949

15f Use $x = \dfrac{x^3 + 2}{5}$ 0·4142135

15g Use $x = \dfrac{6 - x^3}{7}$ 0·7874014

16a $x = -0.155$ $y = 3.59$

16b $x = 2.2444$ $y = -2.0600$

16c $x(3x^2 + 5) - 1$ 0·186501

16d $x[x(4x - 2) + 3] + 2$ 13·256

16e −0·531625 −3·135041

16f −0·114468 1·549952

16g 1·3282689

16h −2·5445116

INDEX

OTHER GREAT PAPERFRONT BOOKS

Each uniform with this book

PUZZLES AND TEASERS FOR EVERYONE

Written by Darryl Francis and edited by David Pritchard, both well known in "Games & Puzzles" magazine, this brilliant collection of baffling puzzles with over 120 diagrams has a unique random answer system to prevent you cheating; will tax your brain on words, numbers, logic and real life problems. Pit your wits against this stupendous book. 160 pages. 214 puzzles.

WORD QUIZ BOOK

A puzzle book on words that is fun *and* educational. As well as being absorbing fun, you can expand your vocabulary – test your knowledge of words – their meanings, uses, spellings – in this series of head-scratching quizzes by a specialist teacher in English and speech. 128 pages.

CROSSWORDS FOR THE ENTHUSIAST

60 intriguing and varied crosswords to test both dabblers and fanatics, many introduced for the first time by Don Putnam, professional compiler for many years. Thematics and acrostics, anagrams and charades – all included. *Greco:* "Wonderful value." *Ffancy:* "The puzzles are obviously first-rate . . ." *Apex:* ". . . very good value . . ."

YOUR BUSINESS
THE RIGHT WAY TO RUN IT

The joy of having your own business is that to some extent you can control the effect on your life of boom, slump or inflation. Redundancy, the sack, or enforced early retirement need hold no fears for you! But the businessman's disciplines are of a different kind.

Andrew Elliot's University was the Glasgow slump of the '30s. He left school at 16 and started in the timber business.

In a dozen years he had made enough money to retire for a while, and do some highly lucrative part-time writing.

After the war, he started again from scratch, this time as a book publisher. Paper was rationed; money was tight. Elliot knew not a single printer, author or bookseller. Bold? Yes, but it worked, and today his firm, **Elliot Right Way Books** is famed throughout the world for low-priced practical books.

Elliot cherishes Private Enterprise and hopes to encourage new ventures with this book, which is co-written by his elder son Clive.

EASYMADE WINE AND COUNTRY DRINKS

As little as a few pence a bottle can be the cost of wines made from these recipes, specially compiled by world expert, Mrs. Gennery-Taylor, for **simplicity** and **economy.** These are straightforward country recipes which have stood the test of years, and the ingredients can be easily found in field and hedgerow.

No expensive equipment is required. All you need is a large saucepan or preserving pan, a couple of plastic buckets, fermentation jars and some bottles with corks. This new edition of the book has been fully revised and largely re-written to take into account the most modern developments in home wine making.

Includes a wine calendar to let you know when to make each wine throughout the year.

THE HOME MEDICAL ENCYCLOPEDIA

Many medical books seem to be specially designed to leave the patient in abject fear and terror. Not so "The Home Medical Encyclopedia", which is written in a friendly and optimistic way, and gives very real and valuable advice to anyone with an illness in the house.

All illnesses and medical terms appear in A-Z order for simple reference. The easy-to-understand way in which this complex book is written is a triumph, and the book is free of medical phrases unfamiliar to the layman.

The text was specially and authoritatively re-revised, and the entire book re-set for the first paperfront edition.

CAR DRIVING IN 2 WEEKS

MONEY BACK GUARANTEE...

If you fail the Driving Test, or if you disagree that this is one of the greatest, best illustrated, most instructive books ever on the subject, return to publisher for refund.

The original author was formerly a Branch Manager with the British School of Motoring Ltd. and later founded the **Right Way Schools of Motoring.** The book has recently been completely revised and re-written to comply with the most modern practice.

Can save pounds in lessons. Makes learning easy. Accepted as the Standard Work – Some reviews:

Daily Telegraph: "Immensely practical."
The Motor: "A book worth having."
The Autocar: "No learner could fail to benefit."

MORE GOLF SECRETS

Dr. H. A. Murray's first classic *The Golf Secret* deals mainly with the swing and with numerous golf fallacies. This sequel is written in the same critical strain, fills in the "gaps" which were left in the original work, but is complete in its own right.

The book enables the reader, even a novice, to see a clear way through the contradictions in professional teaching about the grip, the stance, and many other things. It explains the scientific basis of golf, unhindered by doubt and difficulty.

Some reviews which hailed the publication of Dr. H. A. Murray's first great classic *The Golf Secret*:

The Field: "The biggest contribution for many years to better golf."
The Scotsman: "The long-sought secret."

THE RIGHT WAY TO KEEP PONIES

Whether you are thinking of getting your first pony, of buying one for your children, or whether you have a pony already, this book is planned to improve your knowledge and provide the information necessary to keep the animal in tip-top health.

Hugh Venables is a veterinary surgeon with many years' experience of horses and ponies.

From the basic decision about whether to have a pony at all, he leads on to the questions of where to keep it, how to house it, where to bed it down, and how to equip a stable. He tackles enthusiastically the questions of the quantity of grass and extra food needed. Winter and Summer. He highlights such important matters as clipping and clothing and the pony's tack. His chapters on veterinary care and on care of the feet and legs are masterpieces of their kind.

BEGIN BRIDGE

Begin Bridge delves to the heart of each skill that the beginner needs and explains each difficulty with relentless clarity.

G. C. H. Fox is an English International player and winner of several national events. He is principal of the Mayfair Bridge Studio, the oldest-established bridge school in England. He is Chief Training Officer of the English Bridge Union's Teacher Training Scheme and has been Bridge Correspondent of the *Daily Telegraph* since 1961. He is a regular contributor to *Bridge Magazine*.

Sunday Telegraph: R. A. Priday says, "... excellent value ... outlines clearly the basic principles of bidding, play and defence."

The Observer: Terence Reese says, "A clear and reliable introduction for the complete beginner."

CROSSWORDS FOR THE DEVOTEE

This square dealing puzzle book is crammed with 55 superior crosswords to set your brain whirring. Each section preceded by Author Don Putnam's commentary. *Games & Puzzles:* "... every answer ... in an explanatory form ... will demonstrate precisely how it has been arrived at. All devotees of the crossword, whether recent or experienced, will find something in this book to puzzle, challenge and entertain them to the full."

TEST YOUR WORD POWER

"Is it a real word?" "What's the word for it?" – Just two of the sections in this fascinating book. How does your vocabulary really rate? Huge 128 page value. Test yourself with this brilliant book and find out! You may be very surprised . . .

BEGIN CHESS

Any youngster aged 7 to 90 will love this! Simple, direct and step by step, explains chess with relentless clarity. Fascinating introduction by David Pritchard, Editor of the "Games & Puzzles" magazine. 160 pages. Over 350 clear, concise diagrams.

THE RIGHT WAY TO PLAY CHESS

Tenth edition of this huge world seller by David Pritchard, editor of "Games & Puzzles" magazine. 240 pages crammed with information, examples, moves, opening gambits, powers, and illustrative games. Over 100 diagrams. *Chess:* "The best." *Sunday Times:* "Remarkable." *Illustrated London News:* "The Best."

BRIDGE QUIZ FROM A NEW ANGLE

From two of Britain's leading players and writers, Pat Cotter and Derek Rimington, comes this unique, clear, concise guidance. Selected hands demonstrate bidding features used in modern Acol. Test your own bidding on these hands – try your play – then compare with the experts! 160 pages. Graphically explained answers. 87 questions.

THE RIGHT WAY TO IMPROVE YOUR ENGLISH

Progress in business, profession, or in securing academic qualifications is hindered by inability to use English correctly.

Perhaps there is no need for everyone to have the same magnificent command of our language as Churchill or Shakespeare, but we all need a thorough grounding in the basic elements of English.

J. E. Metcalfe has provided that in this book.

This is not a dull, dry, grammar book but a light-hearted

191

exposé of the various errors which tyro and experienced alike may so easily make.

Contents include: On English . . . Parts of Speech . . . Verbs . . . Pronouns . . . The Sentence and the Paragraph . . . Punctuation . . . Common Mistakes . . . Oddities of the Language etc.

EXAM SECRET

Help for all exams. An astounding book which shakes entire examination systems for Children and Adults! Away with exam nerves! Cut work by 70%. See how you pass, not by swotting, but by technique . . . marvellous memory . . . plan . . . notes . . . concentration . . . the BIG DAY. Tens of thousands helped already.

MATHS FOR MUMS AND DADS

What is eight in base three? Do you know? Bridge that enormous gap between what most young parents were themselves taught at school and what their children are now taught. Valuable advice on how to foster interest in maths, and help both your child and his teacher to consolidate schoolwork. 192 pages.

ELLIOT RIGHTWAY BOOKS KINGSWOOD, SURREY, U.K.